PETER SELG was born in [ ] medicine in Witten-Herdecke, specializing in paediatric and adolescent psychiatry and psychotherapy. He is the Director of the Ita Wegman Institute for Basic Research into Anthroposophy in Arlesheim, Switzerland, and Professor of Medical Anthropology at the University of Art and Society in Alfter, near Bonn. He is the author of numerous books on the humanities, anthropology, medicine, education and biographical history. Peter Selg is also involved in extensive teaching and training activities and the management of public archives, holding the post of Research Associate at the College of Humanities in Dornach.

Notebook entry by Rudolf Steiner relating to soil conditions and suggested treatments for the Koberwitz estate (Ita Wegman Archive)

The Agriculture Course
Koberwitz, Whitsun 1924

Rudolf Steiner and the beginnings
of biodynamics

PETER SELG

TEMPLE LODGE

Translated from German by Matthew Barton

Temple Lodge Publishing
Hillside House, The Square
Forest Row, RH18 5ES

www.templelodge.com

Published by Temple Lodge 2010

Originally published in German under the title *Koberwitz, Pfingsten 1924* by Rudolf Steiner Verlag, Dornach, in 2009

A catalogue record for this book is available from the British Library

ISBN 978 1 906999 08 7

Cover by Andrew Morgan Design
Typeset by DP Photosetting, Neath, West Glamorgan
Printed and bound in Great Britain by Cromwell Press Group Ltd.

'If I did not need to nurture anthroposophy, I would become a farmer.'

Rudolf Steiner in conversation with Count Polzer-Hoditz

Contents

Introduction

As Rudolf Meyer, a participant in Rudolf Steiner's 'Agriculture Course' put it, the course which was held during Whitsun 1924 at Koberwitz Mansion in Silesia, an hour's train journey from Breslau (now Wroclaw) 'entered the annals of cultural history' as a 'new beginning wrested from the decline of the western world'.[1] Steiner, indeed, conceived his eight Koberwitz lectures on the specialist theme of agriculture not only in a fraught political and cultural situation but also in the face of developments which have inevitably culminated in the 'current desolate state' of agriculture (Herbert H. Koepf). As long ago as the nineteenth century, a sole focus on technology, science and profitability had led to intensified use of chemical products and the swift demise of traditional agricultural skills, and loss of a close relationship with and sensitivity to the natural world. As the twentieth century dawned, bringing with it improved methods of industrial production and intervention (as well as 'an ever more reckless integration of agriculture into industrial and financial systems'[2]) these developments accelerated in a dramatic fashion. As Rudolf Steiner stated back in 1924, the 'blessings' of materialism for agriculture were and remain deceptive. All the structures and ways of life which had gradually developed over many centuries amongst the community of farmers were crumbling— along with the intrinsic quality of their produce. Back in Dornach Rudolf Steiner said:

Indeed, not many people know that during the last few decades the agricultural products on which our life depends have degenerated extremely rapidly [...] It is not only human moral development that is degenerating but also what human activity has made of the earth and of what lies just above the earth. This degeneration can be confirmed statistically and is the subject of discussion in agricultural organizations, and yet it seems that nothing can be done about it [...] This is a cosmic issue as well as an earthly one. Precisely from the example of agriculture we can see how necessary it is to derive forces from the spirit, forces that are as yet quite unknown. This is necessary not only for the sake of somehow improving agriculture but so that human life on earth can continue at all, since as physical beings we depend on what the earth provides.[3]

Rudolf Steiner spoke about the decline of 'instinctive farming wisdom'.[4] What had guided the feelings and actions of farmers for many centuries largely disappeared with the rise and scientific application of materialism, and by the third decade of the twentieth century was already consigned to the past. 'Exhaustion of traditions', according to Steiner, also however went hand in hand with 'exhaustion of the soil', for increasing plundering of resources by profit oriented agriculture was leading to an ongoing loss of life forces in produce:

> [...] the traditions are vanishing. People fertilize scientifically now; and the grains and potatoes and everything else become worse and worse.
>
> People know this, they confirm it statistically, yet today there is nothing but resistance to practical measures that derive from spiritual vision.
>
> It is tremendously important to have some insight when it comes to things like this.[5]

Rudolf Steiner was not some melodramatic alarmist. It was however palpably clear to him—and to a few other far-sighted people in the first decades of the twentieth century—that the 'improvements' in agriculture achieved through intensive use of chemical fertilizers and pesticides, through large-scale monoculture, uprooting of many elements of the natural landscape and numerous 'technological innovations' were only of apparent benefit:

> So we must look for a due distribution of wood and forest, orchard and shrubbery, and meadow-lands with their natural growth of mushrooms. This is the very essence of good farming, and we shall attain far more by such means, even if we reduce the area available for tillage to some extent.
>
> It is no true economy to exploit the land in a way that rids us of all the things I have mentioned here, in the hope of increasing our crops. Your large plantations will become worse in quality, and this will more than outweigh the extra amount you gain by increasing your tilled acreage at the cost of these other things. You cannot truly engage in a pursuit so intimately connected with nature as farming is, unless you have insight into these mutual relationships [...][6]

Despite these warnings, however, destruction of the natural environment continued apace in order to maximize production, though not, contrary to appearances, with any corresponding enhancement of the quality of produce:

> The farmer may not always be aware of it; but unconsciously this is the underlying thought. He is astonished when by some measure he gets great results for the time being—say he gets big potatoes; or anything else that swells

and grows large in size. But he does not pursue the investigation far enough beyond this point.

In fact this is not the most important thing at all. The important thing is that when such produce reaches the human being it should be life-enhancing and health-giving. You may cultivate some crop or fruit that is absolutely splendid in appearance, and yet, when it is consumed it may only fill the stomach without promoting human life. The science of today is incapable of pursuing the matter to the point of finding how to provide the best kind of nourishment for the human organism. It simply does not find the way to go about it.[7]

Why, for example, is it no longer possible to find potatoes as good as the ones I ate when I was a boy? That is simply a fact; I've tried it everywhere. Not even in the country districts where I ate them then can one now find such potatoes. The nutritional value of many things has declined, particularly in recent decades. The more intimate influences at work in the universe are no longer understood.[8]

It was clear to Rudolf Steiner that the chemical fertilizer 'path' is not that of an agriculture of the future. What was needed instead was new, conscious insight into life forces and laws, into the nature of organisms, into the diverse realms of nature, and the determining factors of both earth and cosmos that influence them. Agriculture works in, with and for the realm of life—and the old 'instinctive agricultural wisdom' was imbued with this sense and had perpetuated it through long traditions. Drawing on ancient 'instincts', farmers had handled life forces with care and respect, observing numerous rules and traditional guidelines which determined what they did and did not do from sowing through to harvest. This cultural heritage was widely suppressed and dismissed in the nineteenth century, a period which—according to Steiner—was the spiritual 'culmination' of materialism. In 1924, when Rudolf Steiner held his Koberwitz course, the end of 'traditional' agriculture was not merely in sight, but had already become reality in many places, although genetic modification and many further industrial and political interventions were still to come. 'Koberwitz' thus marked an attempt to launch a radical new impetus in this situation; and, based on spiritual science, to found a new, truly ecological agriculture working out of specific and detailed insight into both the micro- and macrocosmic requirements of a healthy agriculture, thus working 'positively in harmony with the whole cosmos'.[9]

Rudolf Steiner intended that the perspectives opened up at Koberwitz should be implemented with all force and intensity—especially the new approaches, whose details he had specified, to organic fertilization and the enlivening of the earth. Ehrenfried Pfeiffer wrote as follows about a conversation with Rudolf Steiner in Dornach that took place directly after Steiner's return from Koberwitz:

> When asked whether one should initially run introductory trials on the new method, he replied thus: 'The most important thing of all is that the blessings of the preparations should be brought to the widest possible acreage throughout the globe, also in order to improve the nutritional quality of agricultural produce in the most widespread and comprehensive way. That's what one should focus on. You can always run such trials at a later stage.'[10]

Rudolf Steiner also said to Pfeiffer:

By mid-century, spiritual scientific insights must be put into practice if unspeakable harm to the health of nature and the human being is to be avoided.[11]

*

Although the underlying mood of the Whitsun course at Koberwitz was light-filled and future oriented, the problems rife in civilization were a (largely unmentioned) background to what Rudolf Steiner presented. In his Breslau karma lectures, he briefly touched on anthroposophy's 'cultural and historical task' in relation to existing East–West problems, even hinting at the possible end of western civilization, and speaking of its (potentially) 'terrible fate'.[12] During lunchtime conversations at Koberwitz (an 'island of order and calm'[13]), likewise, Rudolf Steiner repeatedly stated that *'Europe is sitting on a volcano, and is unaware of it'*. Rudolf Meyer noted:

> He said this, during these days, out of profound concern for our western civilization. Between the course events, at mealtime conversations, one could hear Rudolf Steiner referring to the brewing world storm as something that could no longer be averted. He spoke of the destruction of Central European cities.[14]

For most people around Rudolf Steiner such words not only appeared alarming but also alienating, and seemed far removed from agricultural tasks and concerns. Yet for Steiner this perception was a signature of the times; a figure of contemporary conditions which related to agriculture and yet went far beyond it: 'Today we not only face the decline of the West in relation to soul culture, but this also penetrates deep into the other kingdoms of nature, for example in relation to agriculture.'[15] The destructive processes at work in Central European civilization, which were to erupt 15 years later in the Second World War, were already clear to Rudolf Steiner in 1924. The political, economic and industrial situation in Central Europe—especially in Germany—was difficult and tense. While the currency reform in November 1923 had succeeded in halting inflation, in real terms wages had declined, and unemployment stood at 11 per cent in Germany. Five and a half years after the end of the First World War, almost a sixth of Germans lived on state welfare. A hitherto unknown concentration of businesses determined what was happening in Germany: a few, powerful conglomerates dominating the market, driving the rationalization process and the mechanization of production, with a consequent loss of workplaces. Shortly after his return from Koberwitz, Rudolf Steiner briefly reported as follows on his visit to the estate:

> We saw all there was to see [on the estate], including, of course, some signs of Central Europe's collapsing economy. The Koberwitz estate is admirably run, and farming has to continue regardless, but the economic situation in Germany is certainly terrible.[16]

At one point in the Agriculture Course, Steiner said:

> You see, this modern cultural and intellectual life has taken on a very destructive form, especially as regards the economic realm, though very few are as yet aware of its destructiveness.[17]

Three months before the start of the lectures on agriculture, the trial began of the perpetrators of the November 1923 putsch: Adolf Hitler, General Ludendorff and eight other National Socialists. By the end of the same year, the whole German public was aware of an upsurge of radical rightwing forces that were taking advantage of political and economic instability—even though Hitler's first attempt to overthrow the government did not succeed. The trial in Munich—which rehabilitated Ludendorff after four weeks and released him (temporarily leaving him at the head of the Nazi movement) and brought only the mildest of sentences for the other accused—was a great success for Hitler. He gave agitatory speeches before the assembled press and gained further popularity. During his six months of detention (in luxurious conditions) he received a continual stream of visitors and mail. It was there he wrote the key text setting out his programme, *Mein Kampf*, in which he developed his views on popular nationalism, German ascendancy and an anti-semitic doctrine of annihilation.

By 1924 fascism was already pervasive throughout Europe. Two months before the Koberwitz course, Benito Mussolini's position as *Il Duce* was greatly strengthened in the Italian parliamentary elections by terrorist methods and fraudulent election practices. In Russia, east of Koberwitz, on the other hand, Stalin was consolidating his power after the death of Lenin on 21 January 1924 at Gorki near Moscow. As one of his last actions, Lenin had warned in Stalin's presence:

> Since he became general secretary, comrade Stalin has concentrated immeasurable power in his hands, and I am not convinced that he will invariably know how to make careful enough use of this power.[18]

In 1924—as the year before—the Norwegian parliament's Nobel Prize committee was unable, to general regret, to find a suitable candidate for the Peace Prize. By contrast, in the USA new methods of killing were being tested, which Adolf Hitler was to put into widespread practice from 1943 onwards in Polish concentration camps not far from Breslau. On 8

February 1924, four months before the Whitsun conference began at Koberwitz, a death sentence was carried out for the first time in a gas chamber at Nevada state penitentiary—'in the quickest and most humane method of killing a human being', as its initiator Major D. A. Turner announced to the press.[19]

*

'*Anthroposophical conference in Breslau on the occasion of the agricultural course at Koberwitz*' ran the wording of the joint event for which anthroposophically-oriented farmers were invited to Koberwitz while members of the Anthroposophical Society were to assemble in Breslau. There, each evening after the Koberwitz course, karma lectures, Class lessons, eurythmy performances and a speech course were to take place. The scope of events at Whitsun 1924 was enormous: 'To arrange a conference of this dimension required a great deal of enthusiasm born from the spirit of anthroposophy and a great love for the cause',[20] said Rudolf Steiner in praise of the Count and Countess Keyserlingk, whose house was the organizational focus of all the events. The spiritual-scientific work, though, was Rudolf Steiner's responsibility—and the agricultural lectures were only a part of what Steiner had to accomplish at Koberwitz and Breslau in June 1924, at the age of 63, in poor health and in the last year of his life. On 14 June, in a brief description of one day, he wrote to Ita Wegman:

There's really rather a lot crammed into the programme, I'll just give you an idea by describing the schedule for yesterday. From 8.30 to 10.30 a.m. Dr Engel was here with patients; from 11.30 to 1 p.m. I gave the course lecture for farmers; 2–3 p.m. was the discussion about it—and then

other people came to speak with me. Then the drive to
Breslau; between 6 and 7 p.m. was the Class lesson; 8–9
p.m. the members' lecture. But I'm satisfied with it all. So
many people have come from all over the place; and
Breslau itself already has a good number of members. And
one has to make sure that these people get as much as
possible.[21]

Most of the participants at the agriculture lectures
attended everything—the whole scope of Rudolf Steiner's
lectures at Koberwitz and Breslau, with their diverse
themes, dimensions and highlights. At the end of the conference, Ita Wegman received a report from a doctor who
attended, which ran:

Our glorious Whitsun conference is now over. It was
inexpressibly beautiful [. . .] The agriculture course, which I
was also allowed to attend, was of great, world-historical
importance. Then the many members' lectures, the Class
events, the discussions with young people, the eurythmy
performance—all of it unspeakably glorious. You will hear
all about it—there was also much that was specifically
medical.[22]

Rudolf Steiner's audience—the farmers but also participants from other professions—were deeply moved by what
they heard and experienced. Farmer and Christian Community priest Rudolf von Koschützki, who attended the Agriculture Course with his fellow priests Rudolf Meyer and Kurt
von Wistinghausen, wrote to all the priests as follows:

If I attempt to convey my impression of the divine gift of
these Whitsun days, I have to tell you that this can only be
understood by someone who has been head-over-heels in
love, at least once in his life. If you raise this feeling out of

the sensory into the spiritual realm, then you can get a sense of my overall impression.[23]

Koschützki spoke of the 'divine gift of these Whitsun days' in an elevated or uplifted mood. But Rudolf Steiner too, after returning from Koberwitz and Breslau, emphasized the Whitsun character of the whole event: *'And so it was a lovely Whitsun celebration, a truly anthroposophical Whitsun festival.'*[24]

The content of the lectures given at Koberwitz (and also Breslau) was not easy to grasp intellectually; and when Rudolf Steiner met Count Keyserlingk on the stairs after his third agriculture lecture and asked him whether he had understood his (Steiner's) comments, Keyserlingk replied: 'No, Herr Doktor, I didn't understand a word.'[25] Nevertheless, at Koberwitz already, Steiner saw that the farmers listening to him could absorb the future potential of what he was saying in their own way. He found a 'community of open-minded, future oriented and primarily young people'[26] who were moved, in their hearts and will, by the substance of the Agriculture Course to take up the initiative launched at Koberwitz and carry it forwards into the future. It was not Rudolf Steiner but the community of farmers gathered at Koberwitz who established biodynamic agriculture as a social reality, based on the precedent of the shared 'Whitsun experience' at Koberwitz,[27] at a difficult historical period and in the face of ominous signs of gloom. At Count Keyserlingk's estate Rudolf Steiner spoke of 'unconditional work'. The group of farmers was prepared to do this common work—each in his own I, on his own behalf and with individual presence of mind, yet also in mutual connection.

Rudolf Steiner was very pleased and hopeful about these developments, and spoke of 'the agriculture course, which I believe was quite *fruitful*.'[28] After Koberwitz, despite many worries, Rudolf Steiner was buoyant on his return to Dornach—'because it shows the real possibility of bringing something originating in anthroposophy right into practical life'. He went on to say, in relation to what he experienced at Koberwitz:

> ...it is possible for anthroposophy to work from both the most highly spiritual side and from the most practical. In actuality we are only working in the right way when these two sides are woven together in complete harmony. When we work anthroposophically, it is all too easy to make the mistake of not letting things on the spiritual side break through into real life, of having them remain as some kind of theory or mere faith in the words—not even faith in the thought content, but faith in the words. We fail to grasp the fact that spiritual things can really enter into immediate, practical life.[29]

At the same time Rudolf Steiner knew that anthroposophical farmers—like the doctors, teachers and curative educators—were only at the beginning of an arduous path. 'That is the point, my dear friends—*do not lose heart; know that it is not the momentary success that matters; it is working on and on with perseverance.*'[30]

*

The aim of this present monograph is to convey a general sense of the situation and atmosphere, the context within which the course took place, highlighting some of its intentions—as well as those of the framing lectures in Breslau—and drawing on the available literature and numerous archive materials. A fair amount has been published in relation to Rudolf Steiner's agricultural lectures, as general overview and for introductory purposes, as well as in more specific detail. In 2001, after decades of research, Herbert H. Koepf succeeded in describing the whole course of biodynamic agriculture's development and history in the twentieth century.[31] The specific and limited remit of this present volume is to focus on Rudolf Steiner, on the origins and realization of the course; in other words, it attempts to approach a spiritual life process that occurred in 1924 but whose reverberations can, to a certain degree, still be felt today. 'Koberwitz' was and is one element of Rudolf Steiner's achievements, and of the unfolding of anthroposophy in the situation that prevailed at the beginning of the twentieth century as a new kind of mystery knowledge. Five months after the School of Spiritual Science was founded in Dornach, the Koberwitz course formed part of Rudolf Steiner's efforts to allow this new knowledge to benefit diverse areas of life, and the people working in them and seeking renewal. At the time Rudolf Steiner embarked on this venture, he was not sure how far it would succeed. If one studies his comments one gets a vague sense, at least, that he was also very pleasantly surprised by the 1924 Whitsun days at Koberwitz—not just by the participants' openness but also by the scope of spiritual insights he himself was able to develop.

The focus attempted here on the *totality of the conference* at Koberwitz and Breslau—that is, the outline of events which took place parallel to the agricultural lectures and were directly connected with Rudolf Steiner—aims not only to give a flavour and partial experience of the spiritual atmosphere of those special June days in 1924, but is also justified by the range of experiences of participants, including 80 farmers. By absorbing Rudolf Steiner's other presentations as well—and experiencing Rudolf Steiner himself—'Koberwitz' became for them far more than 'only' the content of the eight lectures on agricultural practice which they had come to hear. In my view, it is important to consider that the inner motivation, and possibly also the helping powers needed for realizing the new agriculture, arose from the *totality* of people's perceptions at Koberwitz and Breslau, from the trust and connection with that anthroposophy which Rudolf Steiner represented and lived in exemplary fashion, and, indeed, embodied. It is also worth reflecting that young people largely sustained future oriented developments in June 1924. Rudolf Steiner also addressed this younger generation separately at Breslau and Koberwitz, and for many of them the Michaelic character of these striking addresses was life-changing. Some of them began to work in a pioneering capacity within the new agriculture, while others worked in related fields to promote the impetus they had received, with great enthusiasm for the future and a powerful effect on others. If we consider these contexts, our gaze can broaden beyond the agricultural lectures themselves—and ultimately return to them again with new and sharper attention: to their impressive and still innovative greatness and impetus: 'The texts are accessible to a progressive increase in understanding—and require continuous, meditative study. Inner schooling pursues its own, profession-appropriate path.' (Herbert H. Koepf)[32]

*

This book was written and compiled at the Ita Wegman Institute for fundamental anthroposophical research (Arlesheim), where studies are undertaken on the history of Rudolf Steiner's life and work, and on the application of anthroposophy to key areas of life. My personal thanks are due, in particular, to Gerda von Keyserlingk, whose friendship I enjoyed in the last years of her life, and who urged me in very personal terms to read the book her late husband, Adalbert von Keyserlingk, had published in 1974, which was later published in English under the title *The Birth of a New Agriculture—Koberwitz 1924.* In this volume Adalbert von Keyserlingk, son of Carl and Johanna von Keyserlingk, meticulously compiled reports and reminiscences of participants and those helping to run the Whitsun conference, and also revised and abbreviated the memories of his mother Johanna which she had published 25 years earlier in 1949, in a small, cyclostyled edition ('Twelve days with Rudolf Steiner. Transcribed by Countess Johanna Keyserlingk, née Skene of Skene, for my family, from diary pages written during the Agriculture Course'). Johanna von Keyserlingk's memories—like those of other Koberwitz participants—are not without error; yet the special testimony they represent only became clear to me after the death of Gerda von Keyserlingk. No other conference notes were compiled in this way, in good time, from contemporary witnesses during Rudolf Steiner's life. In the case of great, innovative gatherings such as those at Arnhem, Penmaenmawr and Torquay—but also key Dornach events, including the Christmas Foundation Meeting—we lack almost all immediate records of participants' responses. The more clearly one recognizes how spiritually important these events were, the greater is one's sense of omission and irreplaceable loss—for more than merely historical reasons. But 'Koberwitz 1924' was, to a certain extent, documented in good time by Adalbert and Gerda von Keyserlingk, as the only profession-specific School of Spiritual Science course which Rudolf Steiner gave outside Dornach— at the Keyserlingk family residence—after the Christmas Foundation Meeting.

I also want to thank Walter Kugler once again for allowing me to inspect documents at the Rudolf Steiner Archive, and colleagues at Rudolf Steiner Verlag for their helpful collaboration in publishing [the German edition of] this book. Without an invitation from Nikolai Fuchs and Stefan O. Mahlich to speak about Rudolf Steiner and the Agriculture Course at the annual conference of the Agriculture Section at the Goetheanum in 2009, this study would not have been completed when it was, and I therefore thank them in particular for the stimulus they gave.

Peter Selg
Ita Wegman Institute
Arlesheim, December 2008

Letter from Carl von Keyserlingk to Rudolf Steiner, 22 April 1924,
requesting confirmation of arrangements for the Koberwitz course
(Rudolf Steiner Archive)

1

The Prospect of a 'Private Course'

Rudolf Steiner, the farmers and Koberwitz Mansion

I must confess, however, that it was not easy for Count and Countess Keyserlingk to get this course off the ground. It had been promised for a long time, but I did not manage to get there...[33]

At Koberwitz, Rudolf Steiner said of his connection with agriculture:

I grew up entirely amongst peasant folk, and in my spirit I have always remained there—I indicated this in my auto-biography. Though it was not on a large farming estate as you have here, in a smaller domain I myself planted potatoes, and though I did not breed horses, at any rate I helped to breed pigs. And in the farmyard of our immediate neighbourhood I lent a hand with the cattle. These things were very close to me for a long time. I took part in them actively. Thus I do at any rate have a love of farming...[34]

Rudolf Steiner's childhood and teenage years in Lower Austria, in the 'Vienna Basin' parishes of Pottschach and Neudörfl, were spent in close connection with farming and rural life. In Dornach he impressed a local smallholder with his ability with the scythe,[35] and as a child he had been immersed in the old farming traditions and customs, visiting many of the farmers and working with them, with '*a love of farming*'. In his first years as a student at the Technical College in Vienna, Rudolf Steiner encountered Felix Koguzki, a

knowledgeable herb-gatherer and esotericist of the old,
Rosicrucian school:

> He gathered the most diverse plants everywhere in the local
> regions, and could explain every single plant in terms of its
> essential nature, its occult background. This man possessed
> great, occult depths. When one accompanied him on his
> lonely wanderings, or when he travelled to the capital with
> a great number of plants he had collected and dried, in a
> bundle on his back, the discussions one could have with
> him were highly significant [. . .].[36]

According to Steiner, the herb gatherer Feliz Koguzki was
someone 'wholly initiated into the secrets of the efficacy of all
plants and their connection with the cosmos and with human
nature'.[37] Koguzki became a friend and significant interlocutor for Rudolf Steiner, discussing with him things which
Steiner could not express to anyone else, but which already
lived in his soul at the age of about 20.

His college teacher Karl Julius Schröer also harboured love
for the kind of wisdom whose last vestiges could still be found
amongst 'simple folk' at the end of the nineteenth century.
Schröer rediscovered the Oberufer Christmas plays which were
performed in a rural village close to Pressburg from late
medieval times onwards, and often spoke of them with Rudolf
Steiner.[38] At the age of 20, possibly through Schröer who also
undertook intensive research on ethnic languages and folk
songs, dialects and vernacular speech, Steiner encountered the
life work of another 'odd-ball', the erudite village teacher
Johannes Wurth, who had lived in a neighbouring village to
that of Felix Koguzki, but had already died. In a letter to a
friend dated 3 August 1881, Rudolf Steiner wrote enthusias-
tically of his preoccupation with Wurth, mentioning in this
connection his studies relating to a 'farmers' philosophy' which

he wanted to develop in the near future.[39] At Koberwitz, Steiner also returned to this theme, saying in a lecture:

> How much is contained in many of the old folk proverbs! People today might still derive many a valuable hint from such things.
>
> I could have mentioned it in yesterday's lecture. Among the many things I should have done in my present incarnation, but did not find it possible to do, was this: when I was a young man I had the idea to write a kind of 'peasant's philosophy', setting down the ideas of the peasants in all the things that touch on their lives. It might have been very beautiful [...] A subtle wisdom would have emerged—a philosophy expanding upon the intimate aspects of nature—to which the very phrasing would have given expression too. One marvels to see how much the peasant knows of what is going on in nature.
>
> Today, however, it would no longer be possible to write a peasant's philosophy. These things have been almost entirely lost. It is no longer as it was 50 or 40 years ago. Yet it was wonderfully significant; you could learn far more from the peasants than at university. But that was an altogether different era when one lived with peasants in the country [...] Today the whole world has changed. The younger ladies and gentlemen present here have no idea how much the world has changed in the last 30 or 40 years—how much has been lost of the peasants' true philosophy, of the real beauty of folk dialects, containing a kind of cultural philosophy.[40]

*

In earlier anthroposophical presentations prior to Koberwitz, Rudolf Steiner had already referred here and there to the instinctive knowledge contained in old farmers' almanacs. In Berlin in 1909, for instance, in lectures on the anthroposophical view of the nature of the human being, he spoke about temporal rhythms at work in animals, saying suddenly:

> Don't think for a moment that such rhythms have never before been clearly perceived. We will be able to show that it isn't so long ago that people had at least a dim awareness of these rhythms. If you are aware of such things you can discover rules cited in various rural calendars which invoke certain relationships between animals and the land. The farmer of bygone times used to determine all his agricultural practices by observing the rules in almanacs of this kind. An awareness of such rhythms was implicit in the knowledge of peasants and farmers.[41]

The 'farmers' almanacs' which Rudolf Steiner mentioned in Berlin in 1909, were already a relic of the past by 1924—of an irretrievable, bygone age. At Koberwitz, looking back over the evolution of consciousness, Rudolf Steiner remarked:

> You see, the life of peasant farmers through the centuries is today really nothing more than a myth. The soul of this life is something quite different from what science or civilization contains, lifted as it were out of all real existence. The peasant farmer was really more spiritual than today's scholar. And in the sixties or seventies of the last century, one could sense that the kind of spirituality living amongst the peasants and farmers was dying and fading away.[42]

Agriculture, he said, was increasingly 'interwoven' with technology,[43] and no longer lived within the old rhythms, connections and feelings, thus losing its real nature in some respects: *'If you go to today's materialistic science, you won't find much love there for agriculture.'*[44]

In this contemporary situation, it was necessary to find new access to the spiritual foundations and conditions sustaining agriculture. In 1915, a full nine years before the Koberwitz course, Rudolf Steiner said in Dornach:

> The right and only proper path will be for people to accept and acknowledge the guidelines of spiritual science so that, on the one hand, nature can be illumined, allowing us to penetrate nature's veil by means of spiritual principles. Zoology, botany and agriculture must flourish in accordance with the guiding ideas which spiritual science can give, be fertilized as it were by these principles.[45]

*

Count Carl von Keyserlingk first met Rudolf Steiner and anthroposophy shortly after the end of the First World War in Berlin, through his wife Johanna and Eliza von Moltke.[46] Keyserlingk, who was a trained farmer and officer, and had great organizational and social skills, had worked in Budapest as war ministry attaché for food distribution to the German South-East army. At the time of his first meeting with Steiner he was working as director of agricultural estates for a large industrial company group. His father-in-law, with whom he was frequently in conflict, was the chair of the supervisory board of this family firm and later joint-stock company, called 'Vom Rath, Schöller and Skene'. The 18 agricultural estates, which were associated with a sugar processing plant, and were under Keyserlingk's control, lay south of Breslau, in the fertile 'black-earth' region of Silesia, and employed over a thousand people.

Keyserlingk, a man 'of simple warmth of heart and modesty', was immediately impressed by Rudolf Steiner's formidable spiritual presence and task ('Oh, do people not see who stands before them?'[47]). According to the testimony of his wife Johanna, he found in anthroposophy the 'forces of regeneration for a Europe in collapse'.[48] Rudolf Steiner also acknowledged and valued Carl von Keyserlingk. In the following period he supported him through meetings and letters in his difficult situation in the company group (which Keyserlingk succeeded in changing into a joint-stock company) and encouraged him to ask for Koberwitz Mansion, which had long been refused him, as a home for himself and his family. In the spring of 1920, at the time of the first doctors' course in Dornach, the move to this residence took place. It had 60 rooms and thus great social potential. Eliza von Moltke was Keyserlingk's first guest. 'I arranged for the letters PSSR (*per spiritum sanctum reviviscimus*) to be carved over the smaller side door—people thought they were the initials of the building firm and took no further notice of them.'[49]

Soon after they first met, Rudolf Steiner asked Carl von Keyserlingk to help supervise the agricultural estates of the anthroposophical joint-stock company 'Der Kommende Tag', whose—comparatively—small landholdings lay in Württemberg, in the Swabian Alps and in the Allgäu district. In the summer of 1920, in a personal letter, Keyserlingk asked Rudolf Steiner whether he, Keyserlingk, should battle on within the Silesian company group despite his ongoing difficulties, or whether he ought to put all his energies into Der Kommende Tag. He said he was willing to put his 'whole strength and personality at your disposal, if this should be your wish'.[50] Carl von Keyserlingk's great efforts on behalf of anthroposophy were certainly in the realm of Rudolf Steiner's 'wishes'—but despite this he strengthened the Count's resolve to carry on in his high-ranking post in Silesia, and where possible to develop this further. According to Johanna von

Keyserlingk, Rudolf Steiner had already told Eliza von Moltke in 1919 that Count Keyserlingk could become Agriculture Minister if the Threefold Social Order movement was successful.[51]

Keyserlingk's anthroposophical and social concerns and initiatives were not viewed favourably at the management levels of Vom Rath, Schöller and Skene AG. Keyserlingk was entrusted with developing the estates into models of high yield and maximum efficiency. At the same time, though, he himself made efforts to transfer employees with considerable future potential 'to the currently existing or still to be created agricultural enterprises of Der Kommende Tag',[52] to develop the social aspect of the Silesian estates, and to support Moritz Bartsch, the leading anthroposophist in Breslau, and the threefold social order alliance in their activities. This included working on the actual estates of the joint-stock company. In his letter to Rudolf Steiner in August 1920, Keyserlingk stated that he wanted 'gradually to introduce the threefold idea to the officials, workers and institutions at our operations here'.[53] To the lasting dismay of his father-in-law, estates director Carl von Keyserlingk was known as the 'Red Count'. His nephew, Alexander von Keyserlingk—who arrived from the Baltic region to work for him—described as follows his social initiatives on the Silesian estates:

At that time he built workers' houses and, to the annoyance of some of the gentlemen, created a 'social section' which was under his sole direction. Every employee could come to him—without having to ask his direct superior—and express his fears, wishes or suggestions. At that time, because of the catastrophic shortage of jobs, it was dangerous to make any complaints. In order to ensure there were no reprisals, a monthly discussion was arranged, to which every estate sent two workers' delegates who could voice their concerns in strict confidence. Shop committees did not exist at that time. This arrangement gave the workforce great assurance and there were never any strikes.

There were three main political camps at the time: Nationalists, Democrats and Communists. If an applicant coming to seek employment pretended to be staunchly nationalistic, in order to create a good impression, Uncle Carl was likely to tell him in a serious but friendly manner: 'Your political views are your own affair. They do not concern us. The only important thing as far as I am concerned is that you carry out your work well and are a decent human being.'

During this inflationary period Uncle Carl introduced a quite new way to pay wages. Although currency lost its value every day, wages were generally paid weekly. Large firms were allowed to mint their own coinage—whose value was a little more constant—which could alleviate the greatest hardship. Huge piles of money lay in these companies' cellars. But Uncle Carl had a better idea than that, one which certainly made a lot of work for the office staff, but was of great benefit to the employees. From one day to the next, what each had earned was calculated not in German marks, but in pounds of rye! It was of no advantage to the firm, but the workers got the equivalent value of their pounds of rye on pay-day. If they then exchanged it immediately, there would be no loss. People could even save without losing out! But of course this led to great difficulties with the firm's financial directors.[54]

*

Rudolf Steiner first visited Koberwitz in 1922, at the end of January and again in May, to support the work of Moritz Bartsch when anthroposophical lectures were being given in Breslau. Rudolf Steiner said in a lecture:

> The pleasing progress of our movement in Silesia is intimately connected with the energetic and insightful work done by Principal Bartsch over many years. In his writings, and his always impressive words, he has done what *one* person alone can do to nurture anthroposophy. The Society owes him a great deal.[55]

On his first visit to Koberwitz he wrote a verse in its guest book. About his brief stay at the mansion in May 1922, when he gave a public lecture in Breslau, Johanna von Keyserlingk noted among other things:

> On the journey by car to Breslau, we looked at our fields right and left and I remarked that we were going to have a drought again. Rudolf Steiner said: 'We shall have to reckon with droughts everywhere. In this strip of land, however, it will be a little better.' And after a pause: 'Large estates in any case will find it difficult in future.'[56]

On his departure, Rudolf Steiner promised not just to return but to stay longer the next time. It is not known whether and to what extent anyone at Koberwitz spoke to Rudolf Steiner in January and May 1922 about agriculture. It is very probable however that the social future of agriculture, at least, was an ongoing theme in discussions between Keyserlingk and Steiner. For years Steiner had been preoccupied with the question of how to free soil and land from being seen as just a commodity, and how agriculture should be integrated into a new way of organizing economic life.

In October, directly after The Christian Community was

founded, Rudolf Steiner recommended that the priest Rudolf Meyer should go to Breslau. For several years thereafter, Meyer was a houseguest of the Keyserlingks at Koberwitz, as, later on, were his colleagues Rudolf von Koschützki and Kurt von Wistinghausen. Friedrich Rittelmeyer and Emil Bock had also visited in preceding years, to hold preparatory discussions for founding the 'Movement for Religious Renewal'. Koberwitz Mansion was the first place in Silesia where the Act of Consecration of Man was held.

*

Count Carl von Keyserlingk was not the only farmer or estate owner with whom Rudolf Steiner repeatedly discussed agricultural matters prior to 1924 or whose lands he visited. The influential counts and estate owners Otto von Lerchenfeld and Ludwig von Poltzer-Hoditz were likewise very close to Rudolf Steiner's anthroposophy and, like Keyserlingk, pursued broad socio-political interests and motives. We do not know to what extent Rudolf Steiner had a hand already prior to 1924 in supporting changes implemented at the Köfering estate near Regensburg, which Count von Lerchenfeld had inherited back in 1908, a year after he first encountered Rudolf Steiner. At Koberwitz, however, Steiner mentioned that the estate had 'spiritually' maintained itself, 'whereas all around, the world was plunging into materialistic excesses. That is certainly a phenomenon.'[57] And he spoke humorously of the path that had been accomplished there 'from the anthroposophical transformation of the estate owner to the anthroposophical transformation of the estate'. It is not however quite clear what he meant by the 'anthroposophical transformation' of that estate, from which came the roses for the first performance of Rudolf Steiner's first Mystery play in Munich (on Ascension Day 1910).

We do have testimony, in contrast, of Rudolf Steiner's many discussions with another farmer, Ernst Stegemann. Born in 1882, Stegemann was 24 when he encountered theosophy and Rudolf Steiner in 1906. Later he took a lease on the Marienstein monastery estate, close to Göttingen, which he farmed. It had fields in the valleys along the river Leine, but also high and only awkwardly accessible areas. Rudolf Steiner repeatedly visited Stegemann. At Koberwitz, Steiner did not detail what 'has been discussed between myself and him [Stegemann] over recent years in relation to all sorts of guidelines for agriculture'.[59] As early as autumn 1920, however, Rudolf Steiner pointed the young chemist Johann Simon Streicher in Stegemann's direction, in response to his enquiries into fertilizers and problems connected with them. Stegemann was deeply concerned about the quality of the soil and agricultural produce, and also about how best to preserve and reinvigorate cultivated plants. By 1922 he had converted the Marienstein estate to organic cultivation (i.e. without conventional artificial fertilizers). In June 1922, Rudolf Steiner had long discussions with Ernst Stegemann in Stuttgart about the nature of the plant between earthly and cosmic forces, as well as about the need to breed wild grasses so as to develop future grains for human consumption, particularly oat grass and North Italian mountain rye, but also mouse barley and couch grass. Steiner encouraged Stegemann to seek out possible wild plants in southern Europe and make efforts to breed them into cultivated plants. This conversation made a deep impression on Stegemann. Rudolf Meyer wrote:

I still remember how he came up to me in Stuttgart after this conversation and, deeply moved, began to tell me what the content of his life and work should be from now on. This was nothing less than the task he had been given of breeding new types of grain from grasses. After he had spoken to Steiner of certain more intimate observations he had made in this direction, and expressed his concerns, Steiner had more or less said that all our cultivated plants would grow exhausted as Kali Yuga ended, and it would be necessary to breed new types. He also immediately gave him practical instructions for doing this—how, for instance, a strong variety of oats could be developed from a certain type of grass, and would subsequently produce a healthy loaf of bread.[60]

Two months after the Stuttgart discussion, on 2 August 1922, Ernst Stegemann wrote to Rudolf Steiner from his monastery estate:

My dear Herr Doktor

In our conversation in Stuttgart in June, when you had the goodness to suggest enhancing oat grass through cultivation, you told me I might write to you in regard to the breeding of other plants too, as food for human beings. I would gladly come to Stuttgart whenever you are next there, to receive further guidelines from you about this.

The preparations for cultivating oat grass have been undertaken, and I would be very pleased to start on further cultivation work in relation to substitutes for potatoes, rye, wheat and barley.

I would be glad if you could allow me time for a conversation in Stuttgart when you are there, which according to the management of Der Kommende Tag will be around 10–12 August.

There is no need to reply unless it will be impossible to discuss this with you at that time.

With profoundest esteem and in gratitude, your

E. Stegemann[61]

Ernst Stegemann was filled with a great earnestness for, and spiritual awareness of the tasks to be accomplished, whose moral and esoteric aspect were particularly close to his heart. At their meeting in June 1922 Rudolf Steiner also gave him a plant meditation. Almost two years later he returned to this theme in a letter to Steiner, writing on 11 May 1924, just four weeks before the start of the Koberwitz course:

My dear Herr Doktor

In June it will be two years since you were so good as to give me esoteric content in relation to human beings' relationship with the plants.

In the meantime, here at Marienstein, we tried to realize this human connection with plants. This work (a report on which is now with the Goetheanum executive committee) has attracted various people, both younger and older, who recognize that only a continued deepening of our esoteric stance can prevent the further decline of our agricultural plants.

These people, initially few in number, also recognize that a connection with the plant realm can only gradually arise by strengthening our inner life, raising the ethical level, and through esoteric work.

In this small group we perceive our strong obligation to engage with the plant world, and indeed with all of nature in a creative way; to bring towards the plants out of our inner core the forces which are able to gradually develop weeds into foods. Indeed, we sense that new plants will have to be brought to earth from the world beyond, through human spiritual forces.

We know how inadequate our strength is for this task, yet we find the courage to continue this work we have begun.

Esteemed Herr Doktor, we ask you to give us further esoteric insights relating to the path we have embarked on, of working upon the realm of plants.

Can you tell us what esoteric stance one should have towards plant pests? And also how one should regard the various illnesses of the animal world esoterically?

We know that all illnesses are rooted in the soul and spirit, and warmly ask you to share with us the deep fruits of your spiritual-scientific research on these matters, since we ourselves are unable to carry out such research.

In profound esteem

Ernst Stegemann[62]

Eight weeks previously, in his report to the executive council in Dornach on 5 March 1924, Ernst Stegemann had written about the trials begun at Marienstein for sustaining agricultural plants and for breeding new ones. According to Stegemann, from autumn 1923 trial beds had been planted to explore various issues such as the significance for plant growth of sowing time in relation to the phases of the moon; and also whether the effect of the moon could be enhanced 'if someone who sows the seed forms a conscious connection with the ether streams of the cosmos, and by his inner stance attempts to convey these streams to the grain'. In addition, they tried to discover through experimental test series whether any effect on plant growth could be discerned 'if two people between whom an exchange of etheric forces occurs, pass each other seeds for sowing'. Alongside such questions, Stegemann also outlined his trials relating to suggestions by Steiner for breeding new grains from wild grasses. The letter stated, among other things:

Oat grass was sown on 18.10.23 and on 2.10.23, and in spring is now to be fertilized with potentized earth from cow horns, which have been buried in the earth *since April 1923*.

For this cultivation trial we used the seeds of:
  secale montanum
  horteum spontaneum
  triticum orientale
from the various botanical gardens of Europe; and these are now to be developed into agricultural plants through the use of potentized earth and human influence.[63]

*

Ernst Stegemann sent his letter of March 1924 to the executive council of the General Anthroposophical Society, clearly wishing to give due heed to the developments which had begun with the Christmas Foundation Meeting of 1923/24: the responsibility of the esoteric executive council for initiatives of the newly founded School of Spiritual Science and its Sections. In addition, Stegemann knew that trials had been undertaken in Dornach for several years in close connection with agricultural questions. The young academics Ehrenfried Pfeiffer and Guenther Wachsmuth, in particular, who had been in Dornach since 1920 and were frequently in touch with Rudolf Steiner, were overseeing the initiatives there. Pfeiffer had arrived at the Goetheanum in the spring of 1920, aged 21, and alongside his work at Dornach was also studying science in Basel. Decades later he described as follows his questions to Rudolf Steiner and the beginning of the 'Goetheanum research institute':

Materialistic science is based entirely on the *analytic* method, of splitting apart (nowadays of splitting the atom and nucleus), of disintegration and separation, of fragmenting and all such procedures which are compelled to destroy and take things apart in order to work on the corpse rather than to help things to grow, develop and synthesize. The fact that the human spirit is imprisoned by these methods of dissection is, as I perceived it, the cause of our current situation. Thus my question was: can a different force or energy be found in nature which bears within it not the tendency to atomize and analyse but to build up and synthesize? Would we be able to discover those constructive forces which enable things to live and grow? Would we find correspondingly constructive research methods and possibly be able to use such energies for a different kind of technology to power machines? Then, based on the inner nature of such force or energy, we could create a different technology, a different social structure and, instead of destructive human thinking, an upbuilding kind of thinking. Such a force must bear within it the impetus for organic life, just as so-called physical energies bear within them the tendency to split and divide. My question to R[udolf] St[einer] in October 1920 and spring 1921 was therefore: 'Does such a force or energy source exist? Could it be proven or demonstrated? Could a selfless kind of technology be based upon it?'

As these questions were taking shape in my mind I found a lifelong friend in Guenther Wachsmuth, who was reflecting on precisely the same questions.

I had a few conversations with R[udolf] St[einer] on my own, but often there were two or three of us with him to discuss these themes.

To my question I received the following reply: 'Yes, there really is such a force, but it has not yet been discovered. It is what is generally termed ether (but not physical ether): a force which enables things to grow and, for example, is present in the seed as germinal force. Before you can work with this force, you will have to prove its presence. Just as we have reagents in chemistry, you will have to find a reagent for this etheric force. It is also called etheric formative force, for it creates the form, the figure or structure of a living, growing thing. You could try this with crystallization processes to which an organic substrate is added. It will then be possible to develop machines that respond to this force and are driven by it.'

Rudolf Steiner then outlined the principles whereby this force could be used as a new source of energy. On another occasion, in the presence of Guenther Wachsmuth, he outlined the principle of the four etheric formative forces— light ether, chemical ether, life ether and warmth ether— somewhat differently from the way he described these in the so-called heat and light courses given to Waldorf teachers. He also mentioned a book by [Pandit] Rama Prasad entitled *Nature's Finer Forces*, which he said described some of these things.

After this, Wachsmuth wrote his book on the etheric formative forces. My task was to start experimenting. The collaboration that proceeded from this laid the seed for the Goetheanum research institute.[64]

At the beginning of the twenties, after completing his university studies in law, Guenther Wachsmuth began to elaborate a systematic theory of formative forces which was published in Dornach in the first half of 1924 under the title of *The Etheric Formative Forces in Cosmos, Earth and Man: A Path of Investigation into the World of the Living*, with a title-page drawing by Rudolf Steiner. At this point Steiner had already appointed Wachsmuth as leader of the new Science Section of the School of Spiritual Science at the Goetheanum. Ehrenfried Pfeiffer, on the other hand, took particular

responsibility for furthering the experimental trial series. On
Rudolf Steiner's advice he attempted to use sensitive media to
demonstrate the laws, processes and rhythms of life:

> Rudolf Steiner's suggestions were focused on seeking a
> 'reagent' to etheric forces. In other words, to discover a
> natural process that responds so subtly to etheric formative
> forces that diverse forms result depending on the influence.
> [...] In order to find this reagent to the etheric realm, he
> suggested that one try observing crystallization processes,
> adding plant substances and blood to these and observing
> the resulting crystallization. '*I myself cannot yet say what
> you will discover here; you will be surprised at how much you
> will discover.*' This is all that Rudolf Steiner said in relation
> to this theme. And thus a beginning was made. When I tried
> to ask him about how to set up the trial, he invariably said:
> 'The trial set-up is something you must find yourself.'[65]

Steiner repeatedly urged Pfeiffer and Wachsmuth to work
according to precise phenomenological methodology and to
continue to school their sense of nature, also in the field of
experimental trials: 'In future,' he said, 'people will ask about
the extent to which someone *experiences* things when observing a particular set of phenomena—rather than making up
clever ideas or speculating. In experience itself lie the sources
from which knowledge flows.'[66] From the very beginning,
Ehrenfried Pfeiffer was preoccupied with questions of plant
breeding and plant diseases, with agriculture and nutrition.
He recorded as follows his own question and Rudolf Steiner's
innovative reply in a conversation with Steiner during a car
journey to Stuttgart:

> 'Why is it that, despite your fulsome guidance and
> numerous instructions, the spiritual impulse, particularly

the inner path of schooling, comes to such little effect in individual people, and that despite their efforts the people involved have so little spiritual experience to show for it? Why is it, above all, that despite theoretical insight, the will to act, to successfully realize spiritual impulses, is so weak?' *'This is a problem of nutrition. In its present form, food no longer gives people the strength to manifest the spirit within the physical. The bridge from thinking to will and deed can no longer be built. The foods we eat no longer contain the forces they ought to give us.'*[67]

The question of nutrition, according to Steiner, goes far beyond the biological and medical realm, and affects the spirit's anchorage in the physical and earthly. This issue of nutrition, and thus also agriculture would, said Steiner, determine the future of humanity, including its spiritual future.

Based on his own notes and enquiries, in the autumn of 1922 Ehrenfried Pfeiffer asked Rudolf Steiner how his previous trials undertaken at the Dornach research institute could bear fruit for practical agriculture. In response Steiner suggested that he make specific preparations derived from the animal and plant worlds, and process them by certain means into a soil dressing:

> These substances were to be exposed in a particular way to the rhythms of cosmic and earthly forces in summer and winter, in such a way that life-enhancing energies would be concentrated or accumulated, which could then be used in agricultural practice in very fine dispersion, but with great dynamic effect [...] I still vividly recall the astonishment when Rudolf Steiner advised us to procure cow horns, for instance, to fill these with certain substances then bury them somewhere close by, and leave them to overwinter

there below ground. Naturally, after our first amazement faded, we immediately asked numerous practical questions about this, for instance whether the filled horns should be sealed at the top before being buried, with cloth or wax etc., how long the overwintering period should be, how deep they should be buried, etc. He immediately and specifically answered all these questions, precisely describing what should be done or not done. In relation to what shouldn't be done, I still remember, for instance, my question as to whether one also ought to add metal supplements to the animal and plant preparations. At this Rudolf Steiner gave us a very instructive colloquium on the harmful nature of certain chemical products used in modern fertilizers and pesticides. For example, in reply to my question about mercury, he said that its use would result not only in damaging influences on food itself but also on future generations, and ought therefore to be definitely avoided.[68]

By no later than 1923—not far from the Goetheanum, and possibly at the same time as Ernst Stegemann—Guenther Wachsmuth and Ehrenfried Pfeiffer started work on these horn-manure and horn-sand preparations which Rudolf Steiner would describe in detail at Koberwitz. Wachsmuth wrote as follows about digging up the fertilizer preparations that had rested through the winter of 1923/24 in the Sonnenhof garden at Arlesheim and which, in the late spring of 1924, shortly before Steiner's departure for Koberwitz, were to be retrieved from the ground:

In our enthusiasm when burying the preparations in a meadow we had forgotten to mark the spot carefully, and so when spring came and Rudolf Steiner appeared in person to witness them being dug up, we couldn't immediately find them. [...] Smiling cheerfully he watched as we dug and sought in some sweat and anxiety, for we definitely wanted him there when the first preparations were raised from the ground. After we had dug over quite an area in desperation, and he was just about to get back in the car, the spade fortunately hit upon one of the buried horns, which was now brought to light and which he examined very carefully. Then he called for a bucket of water, into which he shook the overwintered substances, and energetically began to stir the water in spiral movements. [...] We took turns with the stirring, and as we did so he explained in detail how long and in what way the mixing and stirring should continue.[69]

Rudolf Steiner stirred the mixture with Ehrenfried Pfeiffer's walking stick in an exemplary, methodical way: 'He was concerned primarily to stir energetically, form a vortex and swiftly to reverse the direction of spin—that is, the vortex formed by this energetic stirring.'[70] 'Then he briefly showed how the stirred preparation should be sprayed, and what area of soil could be treated with the available quantity (demonstrating this with a hand movement over the garden).'[71]

*

We do not know to what extent the preparations developed in Dornach, and proposed by Rudolf Steiner to Ernst Stegemann no later than the spring of 1923, were actually used on the estates of Der Kommende Tag. The activities of Pfeiffer and Wachsmuth were limited to Dornach, and Ernst Stegemann worked in his own particular way on his leased monastery farm within a small, local community. There was, however, a connection between the work done on the Württemberg estates and the 'Biological Institute' run by Lili Kolisko in Stuttgart which (like the Stuttgart Clinical-

Therapeutic Institute and its associated research laboratory) was also part of Der Kommende Tag's joint-stock company. Already in the early summer of 1920, Lili and Eugen Kolisko had started work there on developing a medicine for treating foot-and-mouth disease, the rationale for which had been suggested to them by Rudolf Steiner, and which was successfully used on Der Kommende Tag's estates.[72] Limited work was also carried out on botanical and agricultural questions at the research centre of the Stuttgart Clinical-Therapeutic Institute. At Rudolf Steiner's suggestion, Ludwig Noll was involved in cultivating medicinal plants, using specific fertilizer metals—a procedure that Steiner told Ehrenfried Pfeiffer must be strictly reserved for medicinal plants:

> Rudolf Steiner emphasized [...] that this only applied to medicinal herbs, and that under no circumstances might one add metals to preparations for food plants. He highlighted the fundamental difference between plants intended for medicine or for food. This was such a stark difference, he said, that a plant raised as a medicinal plant could lose its efficacy if it was fertilized like a food crop. In contrast, using metals on food crops could have a damaging effect on health.[73]

Johann Simon Streicher, too, who had asked Rudolf Steiner in the autumn of 1920—during the first Dornach School of Spiritual Science course—about the relative merits of mineral fertilizer, worked in subsequent years at the Stuttgart research centre of the Clinical-Therapeutic Institute on a fertilizer salt mixture containing potassium and magnesium together with a digitalis extract. According to Streicher, this modified mineral fertilizer was first used in the spring of 1923 on the estates of Der Kommende Tag, but was also successfully applied by Ernst Stegemann at Marienstein, especially to the latter's grain fields.[74]

*

By 1920 at the latest, therefore, various developments stimulated by Rudolf Steiner (or rather suggested by him in response to enquiries) had started in the field of agriculture in different places through different people. These initiatives were only tenuously related to each other. The question of a course in the general principles of such agriculture had been pondered and posed repeatedly by certain individuals—by Count Lerchenfeld, Ernst Stegemann and others. The real initiative for this, though, finally came from two much younger people, born just before the turn of the century, who had been working in agriculture for only a few years, but with great intensity. These were Erhard Bartsch and Immanuel Voegele.

Immanuel Voegele came from a family of Swabian Pietists, and originally had no connection with agriculture. His father was a notary. Voegele's grandfather, however, had done a little work as a winegrower and often spoke to his grandson about the dangers of chemical fertilizer in gardens and on the land. Shortly before the start of the First World War, Voegele left his home in Schoendorf and, at just 17, embarked on an agricultural training in West Prussia. Called up to the army and wounded, he spent some difficult years hospitalized and recovering, and then met Rudolf Steiner after the war ended when the latter was giving the great Threefold Social Order lectures in Württemberg. These made a lasting impression on Voegele, and he then took up agricultural studies in Hohenheim and at a young age became the manager of Guldesmühle farm near Dischingen, which formed part of the estates of Der Kommende Tag. He listened to Rudolf Steiner speak there about new agricultural methods and repeatedly asked him for advice. Steiner praised Voegele for his approach to composting, and the latter was present when Eugen Kolisko and the vet Joseph Werr successfully treated foot-and-mouth with the support of Rudolf Steiner, and, with Lili Kolisko, set about developing other medicines for animals. At the request of Carl von Keyserlingk, however, Immanuel Voegele moved to Silesia, and from 1921, when he was 24, he managed one of the estates that were under the Count's direction. Immanuel Voegele was present when Rudolf Steiner visited Koberwitz at the end of January 1922. A few months later, in a small circle, he cautiously expressed his view that probably only Rudolf Steiner would be able to help agriculture in a full and comprehensive way, in the form of a specialist course.[75] He said this in conversation with Erhard Bartsch, a son of the Rector Moritz Bartsch, with whom Voegele had made friends on Count Keyserlingk's estates. Erhard was two years older than Immanuel and had already met Rudolf Steiner in 1913, when he, Bartsch, was 18. He too had survived the First World War—as aeroplane pilot—with severe wounds, and like his friend Voegele had been inspired by the threefold initiative in Württemberg, which he was studying and promoting locally. On his return to Breslau, he ran the threefold alliance office there, and organized speakers—but at the same time he trained as a farmer alongside his university studies. Like Immanuel Voegele, Erhard Bartsch worked on Carl Keyserlingk's estates. In his letter to Rudolf Steiner in the summer of 1920, Carl made positive mention of the 25-year-old son of Moritz Bartsch and his plans for a 'consumers' association'. Thus Erhard Bartsch, too, felt very connected with the tasks and current problems facing agriculture—the questions of quality, of dubious pest control methods and of livestock health. He also met Rudolf Steiner again at the end of January 1922 at Koberwitz Mansion. His response to the thoughts of his friend Immanuel Voegele was supportive, immediate and impulsive: '*Let's go for it and get on with it!*'[76]

Immanuel Voegele and Erhard Bartsch belonged to the younger generation of anthroposophists and had suffered and experienced at first-hand the horrors of the front in the First World War—but also the uplifting and potentially healing significance of anthroposophy in relation to difficult post-war social conditions. They knew that Rudolf Steiner's help would be decisive for agriculture and was urgently needed. They therefore decided to support their request to Steiner by collecting the names of farmers interested in anthroposophy, sending out an 'appeal' to them on 22 May 1922, shortly after Rudolf Steiner's second visit to Koberwitz. After duly receiving the replies they then turned to Rudolf Steiner himself in August 1922:

> Farmers belonging to the anthroposophical movement, perceiving the vital necessity of their profession and what anthroposophy means for its accomplishment, very much desire to work in their field along spiritual-scientific lines. The first step to realizing this goal would no doubt be if you, esteemed Herr Dr Steiner, would give the general spiritual-scientific foundations and specific suggestions for engaging with agricultural questions, in a course or series of lectures.[77]

Immanuel Voegele and Erhard Bartsch told Rudolf Steiner that their enquiries had met with a whole-hearted response from anthroposophically oriented farmers and others interested in agriculture. They said that they had already received many questions relating to such a course. They wrote, further:

Based on the questionnaire we circulated, we now have the names of 38 people interested in such a course, of whom 35 belong to the Anthroposophical Society and 29 work in farming or related professions. We enclose the list of names and addresses received. The decision as to who of these may attend will no doubt need to be based on guidelines that you yourself will give.[78]

This letter from Immanuel Voegele and Erhard Bartsch was personally handed to Rudolf Steiner by Ernst Umlauf, the branch manager of the Anthroposophical Society in Breslau. But Rudolf Steiner's response was reticent: '*Yes, an agricultural course will certainly be needed at some point, but for the time being the project does not yet have sufficient strength to sustain it.*'[79] Bartsch and Voegele later received a more detailed explanation of these words from Guenther Wachsmuth, who also held the post of secretary to Steiner in Dornach: 'Rudolf Steiner would be glad to hear whether and in what way his future audience has already formed ideas on the requested theme.'[80] At this, Voegele and Bartsch intensified their work, meeting each other regularly. Other young people wishing to prepare the ground for an agricultural course given by Steiner also joined the small Breslau study group. These included the youth-movement member and chemist Franz Dreidax and a 19-year-old farmer and agricultural student Almar von Wistinghausen, who heard about the Breslau preparatory group from his brother Kurt von Wistinghausen. Erhard's brother Hellmut Bartsch, who ran an estate under Carl Keyserlingk's direction, was also part of this work and group of friends from the beginning.

*

Uncertain about how much time should be spent in preparatory studies—given the difficult political circumstances and the fact that the first Goetheanum had been destroyed at the end of 1922—the group around Erhard Bartsch and Immanuel Voegele finally turned to Count Keyserlingk with a request for help. The idea of a course was also something Carl von Keyserlingk had pondered repeatedly, and may even have mentioned to Rudolf Steiner:

> I remember how, in his cheerful and loveable way—filled with the deepest reverence for Rudolf Steiner—Carl looked at me with his kindly eyes and remarked: 'I do not in the least see why I should not petition our Doctor about agriculture, if he gives such marvellous help to other specialists!'[81]

Together with his nephew Alexander von Keyserlingk, who had been working (with Erhard Bartsch) for some time now in the estates management research department on questions of livestock rearing, Count Keyserlingk had also visited Ernst Stegemann several times in Marienstein, heard from him about the suggestions Steiner had made there, and discussed with him the request to Steiner to hold a course. Looking back on this time, Alexander von Keyserlingk wrote:

> All of us were aware of the fact that the use of chemical fertilizers was making the soil's future, and that of man and animal, look ever bleaker, even though high yields at first disguised the true state of affairs. Owing to increased numbers of nematode worms, the amount of sugar beet one could grow was constantly dwindling—and there was no remedy for this. When we saw from Stegemann's results how well Rudolf Steiner understood this problem, we wanted to learn more about it. We did not know that it would be a whole course of lectures, nor did we guess what

wide perspectives Rudolf Steiner would bring to bear on this subject. We only thought he would give us a few instructions to counteract destruction of the soil's fertility and the diminishing quality of some crops.[82]

During the course of 1923, Carl von Keyserlingk personally discussed a course with Rudolf Steiner—most probably in Dornach and in the presence of the farmer Ernst Jacoby from Auggen—and received Steiner's agreement to hold a course 'in the winter'.

Keyserlingk brought the matter up again in a letter he wrote on 23 November 1923, two weeks after the right-wing radicals' putsch attempt in Munich, at a time of severe political unrest in Germany, worsening inflation and increasingly complex circumstances. The day after the failed Munich putsch by the National Socialists, Rudolf Steiner said, 'If this group makes headway it will mean devastation for Central Europe';[83] and in relation to himself: 'If these gentlemen take power, I will no longer be able to walk on German soil.'[84]

Carl von Keyserlingk wrote to Rudolf Steiner to tell him about the existence of an 'agricultural working group' within the German Anthroposophical Society, which had been founded some time before—'as you no doubt already know'. He reminded Rudolf Steiner of the *private course* that had been mooted for the winter, and sent him a list of 64 possible participants. Keyserlingk highlighted non-farmers on the list in red, and asked Rudolf Steiner to look through it and delete or add names. Then he wrote:

Given the fact that a disinclination towards innovation unfortunately still prevails in German agriculture, and that premature or falsely conveyed information about what people hear in the course you give might well endanger our Society's interests, it is my view that great emphasis should be placed on only allowing members of our Society to participate who are professional farmers and who, in addition, can offer a certain assurance that the insights and ideas we gain from you should not be discussed elsewhere without your permission, except where precise research results allow this.[85]

Keyserlingk proposed Koberwitz Mansion as the location for the event: 'As far as the location [. . .] for holding the course is concerned, let me suggest Koberwitz as a suitable place.' He also recommended holding the course in January or February 1924 if possible, since it would be easiest for professional farmers to get away at this time.

To his disappointment, however, Carl von Keyserlingk received no satisfactory reply to his letter from Dornach. '[. . .] Since Rudolf Steiner was greatly burdened with work, travelling, and lectures, he kept postponing the decision.'[86] At this, four weeks later, Carl von Keyserlingk decided to send his nephew Alexander in person to Switzerland. In his report on the Koberwitz course, Rudolf Steiner said:

[. . .] Count Keyserlingk's nephew came to the Christmas Conference here in Dornach with strict instructions not to return home without a firm commitment from me to conduct the course within the next six months. So when this nephew, who has a knack for making the most unlikely things happen, showed up here under those auspices, he was so persuasive that I told him the course would take place at the earliest opportunity.[87]

Alexander von Keyserlingk himself wrote about his meeting with Rudolf Steiner at Christmas 1923:

When I arrived in Dornach I went straight to the joinery workshop and told Frau Dr Steiner that I would like to have a word with Dr Steiner. I did not have long to wait. He appeared and I said my piece. He at once said: 'Yes, I will come to Breslau and will give lectures about agriculture there.' But I told him that was not sufficient—'I was not instructed to ask if you would come, but when you are coming!' Then Dr Steiner smiled, took out his notebook, turned over the pages and then announced: 'Tell your uncle that I will come to you at Whitsuntide.'[88]

It is not very likely that Rudolf Steiner actually specified the Whitsun date to Alexander von Keyserlingk and sent him back to Koberwitz with this promise ('*I told him the course would take place as soon as possible*'). The further correspondence with Keyserlingk shows, rather, that Rudolf Steiner still did not name a date but did nevertheless express his reliable intention to come to Koberwitz within the next six months.

*

Hope that the course would be held started to evaporate, however, amongst those who had worked hard for years, with great longing, to bring it about, and in their own way prepared it. News of Rudolf Steiner's poor state of health and of the many plans and undertakings afoot in Dornach (related to the founding of the School of Spiritual Science) had reached Silesia, and it seemed ever less probable that Rudolf Steiner, whose arrival they had looked forward to for more than a year and a half, would actually appear. On 24 January 1924, Immanel Voegele once again wrote the following heartfelt plea to Rudolf Steiner:

Dear Herr Dr Steiner

Please forgive me dear Herr Dr if, after all our previously dashed hopes—focused on receiving guidance about agriculture from you—I once again turn to you with the same plea. As long as the possibility still exists of an agriculture course according to spiritual scientific principles, it seems to me that I ought not to cease trying. This is because I believe that fulfilment of my hope will enable me to engage in my profession as a whole human being in a way that accords with the spirit and with reality. The more that spiritual science enables me to become aware of the inter-connections between all existence and of things which the physical senses cannot tell us anything about, the more I feel modern agricultural procedures to be a transgression against nature that I should not participate in because I do not believe I can do so with full responsibility. My anthroposophical outlook leads me to believe that the farmer's task and work involves creating conditions for the secret forces of nature active in mineral, plant and animal kingdoms which will enable these forces to work and unfold in ways which they otherwise cannot. At the same time, the produce resulting from such an approach is needed as agriculture's contribution to humanity's full and proper evolution. A farmer who senses the existence of a certain inevitable relationship between human beings and the kingdoms of nature—the interaction and inter-penetration of the forces of the earth, sun, stars, elementals and all other nature spirits—and who sees these inter-actions and interpenetrations sustaining mineral, plant, animal and human kingdoms, feels a host of questions assailing him at every turn in his daily work to which his current knowledge can supply no answers, and which therefore greatly trouble him as unresolved questions. He senses the fact of these forces and their interworking, yet knows nothing of the way they do so, nor of their essential nature. Since he does not have the guiding insights that can lead him to any goal, his work is plagued by wavering and uncertainty. In relation to other farmers who perceive their path and objectives in clearly defined terms, he stands there with empty hands and, as yet, only a beautiful ideal.

The request I now take the liberty of putting to you, which accords with the wishes and longings of farmers who hope, similarly, for help and insight from spiritual science, is that you, dear Herr Dr, might help us move beyond our uncertainty, giving us a little illumination and showing us the direction in which a farmer ought to seek. If it is already possible for spiritual science to offer guidelines to the farmer, with whose help he can undertake his work in accordance with the laws that obtain in the world, and should come to expression there, and if there are requirements which must be fulfilled before such communication can be given, then I beg you to inform me of this and, if possible, to agree to hold the agricultural course.

With profound esteem and regard
J. Voegele[89]

Eight weeks after Voegele's letter, which in general accorded with, at least, the younger farmers' inmost desire for a course, Carl von Keyserlingk once again wrote to Rudolf Steiner on 20 March 1924—that is, after January and February, the preferred months for the course to be given, had already passed. Keyserlingk asked to be admitted to the First Class of the newly founded School of Spiritual Science in Dornach, and informed Rudolf Steiner that he had heard from Guldesmühle estate in Dischingen that the course could still take place '*after Easter after all*'. Pleased that 'at last the time and duration of the course to be held here is fixed', Keyserlingk asked Rudolf Steiner once again to reply soon to his questions of 23 November, and to make further practical proposals. Organizing such a course involved great labour and expense, and the time remaining was very short if Rudolf Steiner really 'intended to come after Easter'. Keyserlingk asked whether he should find a stenographer, expressed his hope that Steiner would give accompanying lectures in Breslau too ('several lectures, perhaps even connected in a cycle') and asked after Rudolf Steiner's health:

> It was with great regret that we heard that you, dear Herr Dr, have been suffering greatly from physical complaints recently. We all hope that you are feeling much better now, and that we may be certain of welcoming you and your esteemed wife soon after Easter for a longer stay with us.[90]

*

Ita Wegman, who had been working a great deal with Rudolf Steiner during this period, giving him medical attention and seeing him frequently—and was also a member of the esoteric executive committee and leader of the Medical Section at the Goetheanum—only heard two weeks after Keyserlingk's letter, on 7 April, of Rudolf Steiner's intention to travel to Koberwitz and Breslau in the near future, very probably in the second half of April or in May. This would be sandwiched between an educational conference in Bern (due to end on 17 April) and the planned events in Paris (scheduled to start on 23 May). Very concerned, Ita Wegman wrote as follows to Rudolf Steiner, who had gone to a public education conference (with five lectures) in Stuttgart:

> I also have a very big request: to make it possible that no further courses are squeezed in between Bern and Paris. Yesterday I heard about the agriculture course that is to take place. But we still need to finish the [medical] book,

which is no less important than the agriculture course. I am
troubled by this unfinished book which everyone is waiting
for.[91]

Despite Ita Wegman's desperate appeal, however, shortly
afterwards Rudolf Steiner confirmed to Carl von Keyserlingk
that he would come to Koberwitz, albeit at a later date—the
beginning of June.

On 22 April 1924, Keyserlingk thanked Steiner for this
news, and sent a further, expanded list of possible participants who, with two exceptions, belonged to the Anthroposophical Society: 'Now the date has been set, I would be
very grateful if you could let me know your requirements,
the length of the course and the names of those you would
like to attend, together with any other wishes and guidelines.'[92]

Ten days later, on 1 May 1924, Erhard Bartsch also, for the
first time, turned directly to Rudolf Steiner. This was on
behalf of Count Keyserlingk—who was in Berlin—and a
group of people interested in agriculture, 'who in recent
months have been meeting frequently to work together on
preparing the agriculture course'. Erhard Bartsch sent Rudolf
Steiner a large collection of questions from the preparatory
and study group in Breslau (with over 60 points): '*Should the
answers to these questions fall within the scope of the course,
those who posed them would be especially grateful if they could
be discussed.*'[93] The range of questions sent by Bartsch was
wide, and they were divided into various categories (general/
crop and plant cultivation/animal husbandry/animal nutri-
tion/genetics/micro-organisms). They extended from a
request for spiritual-scientific explanations of the old farmers'
almanac ('Please explain the farmers' almanac in detail, give
guidelines for re-introducing it, and practical exercises for its

use'), questions about methods of conserving animal and plant foods and fodder, guidelines for using machines in agriculture through questions about profitability and competitiveness ('What compromises will initially need to be considered in the new approach to agriculture to remain competitive, since currently the market in agricultural produce is measured in quantity rather than quality?') to very specific aspects and problems in agricultural work and current challenges ('In what way should one tackle the problem of combating pests [example of the root crop *nematode heterodera schachtii*]?' 'What deeper perspectives can one draw from anthroposophy for the incidence of animal and plant pests?'). It quickly became clear that the Breslau group was hoping for aids to understanding and strategies for solving very specific problems and tasks ('In the case of potato varieties, especially, what is causing their rapid degeneration?' 'How can we acceptably counteract the signs of degeneration in farm animals and crops?'). At the same time they were also seeking deeper understanding of the underlying conditions necessary for agriculture ('What specific values are to be found in the various organic fertilizers [manure, compost, latrine, liquid manure, refuse and green manure]?' 'Is three-field agriculture the right model for crop rotation?' 'Is there a desirable balance to be achieved between wood, crop field and grass meadow?').

Six weeks before Erhard Bartsch's letter of 1 May, Ernst Jacoby also directed some questions to Dornach, addressed not to Rudolf Steiner himself but to Guenther Wachsmuth and thus to the Science Section. At this time Jacoby was farming an estate in Wiesenthal near Schopfheim. He came from a family of farmers in the district of Marggräfl, and was very keen for the course to be held. He wrote as follows to Wachsmuth on 16 March:

Allow me to ask the Section to consider the following questions:

1) In what way should one take account of cosmic influences when sowing?
2) What should the farmer's approach be to weeds and to combating them?
3) What are the decisive guidelines relating to crop rotation?
4) How can a farmer effectively combat plant diseases?
5) I have a brood mare which the vet says is suffering from phlegmon (left back foot). The vet says it is incurable. Is it possible to find a way of curing this?[94]

*

In the meantime, Count Keyserlingk waited in vain for an answer to the questions he had sent to Rudolf Steiner on 22 April, relating to organization of the forthcoming course. In these circumstances, Keyserlingk decided to send his nephew Alexander to Dornach once again in person, to obtain the desired and necessary answers. At the beginning of the second week in May, Keyserlingk sent a telegram to Guenther Wachsmuth, asking whether Rudolf Steiner was in Dornach and would be able to see Alexander—and received a negative reply: '*Rudolf Steiner currently too busy, will write.*' At this Count Keyserlingk wrote to Wachsmuth himself and asked specific questions, 'the answers to which will determine what we do as regards preparing the agriculture course and other planned anthroposophical events here'.[95] Keyserlingk once again asked for precise dates for the course and for Rudolf Steiner's arrival in Breslau. He wanted to know whether Rudolf Steiner was thinking of giving agricultural lectures every day, and what time frame these would require, how the

Whitsun festival days should be planned, how many members' lectures were envisaged, whether and how many Class lessons Rudolf Steiner was planning, when and under what circumstances Marie Steiner would hold a speech course, and how the conference should be publicized in general. He also asked which executive council members would accompany Rudolf Steiner—and requested a speedy reply...

It is not known exactly when Count Keyserlingk received the desired information from Dornach. On 20 May Rudolf Steiner wrote to him in person, and Marie Steiner also sent him 'guidelines', possibly after Wachsmuth had sent a general reply. Thus in the short time remaining Keyserlingk was able to organize whatever was necessary and draw up a detailed programme. Carl von Keyserlingk sent this—provisional— schedule and announcement of the event ('Participation in the Agriculture Course is only for members of the Anthroposophical Society who work as farmers or who have a special interest in agriculture'[96]) to Rudolf Steiner in Stuttgart on 31 May, asking for Steiner's approval of the programme a week before the event was due to begin, 'despite the fact that, as I am aware, it makes far too many demands in particular on your time and attention, my dear Herr Doktor'.[97] Keyserlingk told Steiner that any changes to the programme he wanted could still be made. In addition, the Breslau youth group and the Christian Community were hoping for 'one or several sessions' with the spiritual teacher. Keyserlingk also again asked for the exact time of Steiner's arrival by train in Breslau.

Count Keyserlingk finally received this latter information by telegraph on 5 June, one day before Steiner's arrival, at which point preparations for the Koberwitz course were largely complete. *'Now I have to say that it hasn't exactly been easy for the Count and Countess Keyserlingk to organize this course...'* (R. Steiner)

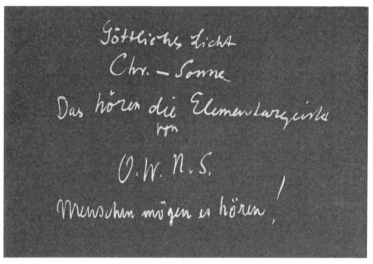

Rudolf Steiner: Rhythm of the Foundation Stone verse. Dornach 31
December 1923 (Rudolf Steiner Archive):
Divine Light
Christ Sun
The elemental spirits hear it
from
E.W.N.S.
May human beings hear it!

2

The Journey Eastwards

The Christmas Foundation Meeting and the arrival in Koberwitz

As it continues and develops, the Anthroposophical Society must become the path towards the renewed mysteries.
Rudolf Steiner[98]

The August 1922 letter from the young farmers Immanuel Voegele and Erhard Bartsch asking Rudolf Steiner to hold a course on agriculture, and listing the names of many interested people, arrived in Dornach at a difficult moment. Numerous anthroposophical initiatives were in crisis in 1922, both financially and also, to some extent, as regarded people's practical capacities and sense of commitment. In Switzerland, liquidation had begun of the anthroposophical 'Futurum AG' company, involving major financial losses. The situation of Der Kommende Tag was also more than precarious, as was the financial situation of the Stuttgart Waldorf School and the Goetheanum in Dornach, whose completion—and still more its actual launch and operations, with the planned scientific research institutes—now seemed very far off. The Anthroposophical Society was weak and no real help—often in fact a burden—for Rudolf Steiner. In November 1922, speaking to members of the Anthroposophical Society in Holland, Steiner described the situation in Dornach as follows:

Construction of the Goetheanum began with enthusiasm. But this same enthusiasm dissipated in the very people who had been enthusiastic to begin with. And now, you can say, these people have left me alone to worry about how things should go on.[99]

Apart from Lili Kolisko's research, Rudolf Steiner was also more than dissatisfied with the scientific work being done in Stuttgart at the institutes of Der Kommende Tag founded for that purpose. The anthroposophical physicians, to whom Rudolf Steiner had given numerous courses and much personal instruction, deeply disappointed him as far as further elaboration of and responsibility for the new medicine was concerned.[100] At the same time, Rudolf Steiner and anthroposophy were the subject of fierce public attack, from scientists, theologians and politicians, in aggressive tirades and polemical texts. His two major lecture trips in May 1922 through numerous cities (also taking him to Breslau, with his last stay at Koberwitz for the time being) were seriously disrupted in various places. In Munich, Rudolf Steiner had a narrow escape when right-wing groups made an attempt on his life. 'The agitation is too potent', he wrote to Marie Steiner on 19 May 1922 from Bremen.[101] The young eurythmist Annemarie Donath described his return to Dornach as follows:

This trip must have been indescribably tiring and aggravating for him. I remember my impression when I saw him again for the first time in the joinery workshop. He stood there in the white working overalls he wore in the studio, behind the stage: he seemed thinner, his gaze more serious and quiet. It felt as though he had returned from a great, arduous and dangerous battle—and the few words he spoke about his trip also reflected this, in all modesty and reticence.[102]

In the second half of 1922, Rudolf Steiner nearly stopped all public lecturing. In the toxic and politically radicalized environment of those times, it was scarcely possible any more to publicly promote anthroposophy.

It does not seem impossible that Rudolf Steiner might have responded differently to the serious and future oriented enquiry from Immanuel Voegele and Erhard Bartsch if it had come two or three years earlier. In 1920—at his own suggestion—Rudolf Steiner began giving systematic instruction to the physicians, supporting the founding of clinics and scientific medical research. For teachers and scientists, too, he gave numerous courses in the first few years after the end of the war, during the founding and development phase of institutions arising from the anthroposophical movement. Given the difficult political circumstances, severe inflation in Germany and the general crisis in the Anthroposophical Society with its fragile institutions and weak public status, it must remain an open question whether Rudolf Steiner thought he could support and take responsibility for the launch of a broader agricultural movement in the midst of this difficult year of 1922. In the field of agriculture, as in other domains, Rudolf Steiner regarded research and empirical enquiry into spiritual-scientific insights as essential, and a one-off course would certainly not be sufficient to make real practical advances. After his experiences with medicine, Rudolf Steiner must have been sceptical about this in 1922, irrespective of the extent to which, at this time, the content of and concept underlying such a course might already have come to maturity in him. Further enterprises and specialist courses did not seem sensible at that moment, or would need to arise entirely from the strength and impetus of professional groups themselves ('Rudolf Steiner would be glad to hear whether and in what way his future audience has already formed ideas on the requested theme'). The developing Movement for Religious Renewal, however, was something that Rudolf Steiner still stood firmly behind in 1922—subject to the proviso that it would be separate from and independent of the Anthroposophical Society—thus facilitating the founding of the Christian Community after a third theology course in Dornach in September 1922.

*

The Goetheanum burned down only a few months later— and to begin with there was no possibility of thinking about anything further. Throughout 1923 Rudolf Steiner struggled with those responsible for the Anthroposophical Society. He repeatedly made clear that a second Goetheanum was only conceivable in the context of a renewed, functioning Anthroposophical Society—and that the real problem, more or less, was the latter's current state. The 'irreplaceable loss of a significant means of making the anthroposophical movement manifest',[103] the destruction of the first Goetheanum would not have been possible, according to Steiner, if the building had been anchored 'in a protecting Anthroposophical Society'.[104] Rudolf Steiner expected positive work from this society, an 'active content' and engagement with tasks 'which people outside it can also respect'.[105] Amongst these 'tasks' Rudolf Steiner also included, not least, pursuing scientific research which he had spoken of for years, repeatedly highlighting angles on possible enquiries and results. 'Recently,' he said, 'I have really not held back from giving positive proposals and suggestions. None of them have been pursued. One gives advice in relation to a particular question, but this is simply thrown to the wind.' On a more positive note, he said during one of the 1923 crisis meetings:

Gradually it will have to [...] happen—provided our research institutes really solve the problems contained in the scientific courses and cycles—that we reach a point where even our opponents recognize that there's something in what we're doing, that they develop regard for the study and research accomplished in the Anthroposophical Society.[106]

Although (or because) the General Anthroposophical Society—or its directorates—did not wake up in the hoped for or expected way in 1923, Rudolf Steiner not only decided to proceed with building the second Goetheanum but also to entirely refound the Anthroposophical Society and its School of Spiritual Science in Dornach. At the age of 62, at Christmas 1923, Rudolf Steiner personally took over the presidency of the General Anthroposophical Society, having previously not even been a member of it, but just an independent spiritual teacher for the old Society. He appointed an esoteric executive, with whose members he could collaborate closely and implement the intentions of the anthroposophical movement: 'It must be an initiating executive, must take up the tasks which the spiritual world asks of the anthroposophical movement; it must take up these tasks and implement them in the world [...].'[107] Rudolf Steiner entrusted the members of the esoteric executive with responsibility for the different Sections or departments (faculties) of the newly founded 'School of Spiritual Science'. According to Steiner, these Sections would in future 'continually accomplish scientific and artistic tasks'[108]—in close collaboration between each Section leader and himself and with those whose professional work fell within a Section's domain of activity. The future School, said Steiner, would research and teach (or train); and this would form the basis for anthroposophy to become effective in meeting the challenges of contemporary civilization in the different spheres of life. Soon after the Christmas Foundation Meeting, Rudolf Steiner incorporated Lili Kolisko's research institute in Stuttgart into the Dornach Goetheanum or School of Spiritual Science ('Biological Institute at the Goetheanum, with head office in Stuttgart'). At the Christmas Foundation Meeting itself, he got Lili Kolisko to give extensive presentations on her scientific research, and subsequently commented:

> But these trials are, basically, all parts or details of a whole as seen from an anthroposophical perspective—a whole which today is really needed very urgently. And if our work continues in the same way as has been undertaken so far at our research institute, then—in 50 or 75 years perhaps—we will arrive at what must really be accomplished: that many parts and details combine to form a whole. This totality will then be of great scope and significance, not only in philosophical terms but also for the whole of practical life.
>
> Today people simply have no idea of how deeply these things could penetrate all practical life: could find their way into the produce which people need, but also, particularly, into approaches to healing and so forth.
>
> Now you might say that humanity's advances have always taken a long time, and it will be no different here. Given the fragility and vulnerability of modern civilization, however, it could well be the case that in 50 or 75 years' time it might no longer be possible to find a way to do what absolutely needs to be done.[109]

In saying this, Rudolf Steiner was also indirectly addressing the future of agriculture: '... *the produce which people need...*'

*

After the Christmas Foundation Meeting, Rudolf Steiner wanted anthroposophy to be represented in the world in a direct and open way, working from its core—without compromises and diplomatic manoeuvres which in previous years had often enough informed the way numerous 'representatives' of the Society conducted themselves:

What we must find is this: we are a small society that confronts the world; and the world—you know which world I mean—does not much care for us. It does not care for us. That is a fact we cannot alter. But nor do we need to do anything to make ourselves as unpopular as possible. I do not mean this trivially, but in a more profound sense, really drawn from the foundations of occult life. If we keep asking what we should do to gain the affections of particular groups in the world that don't care for us; if we ask how we should behave in this or that domain so that we might be taken seriously and respected, then we will quite definitely not be taken seriously. We will in fact only be respected and taken seriously if, at every moment, we feel ourselves responsible towards the world of spirit in what we do; and are aware that at the current stage of human evolution, the world of spirit wants humanity to do particular things in the various domains of life, and that it is up to us to pursue the impulses that come to us from the world of spirit in a clear and true way. Even if this gives offence initially, in the long term it will be the only healing thing. And that is also why we will only establish the right connection with ourselves if we imbue ourselves at every opportunity with the impulses that can come to us from the world of spirit.[110]

For Rudolf Steiner, the 'impulses . . . from the world of spirit' doubtless included the possible—but also necessary—spiritualization of different areas of life, from medicine to agriculture. He had spoken for many years, and with varying emphases, about the need for the 'Christ impulse' to find its way into civilization in specific and tangible ways—not just into Churches and religious denominations. Implicit in this 'Christ impulse' was the transformation of the sciences and humanities in relation to the human being, their real 'Christ-permeation'. The sculptural, artistic figure of the Christ—as 'representative of humanity'—was assigned by Rudolf Steiner to the centre of the first Goetheanum building, and it survived the fire.[111] The Goetheanum was a 'Mystery' building—but its mysteries were those of the future, founded on Christ and committed to the human being. A few months after the Christmas Foundation Meeting, Rudolf Steiner spoke as follows about the task of the Anthroposophical Society:

> The mysteries themselves declined of course during the period in which freedom had to take up its place in human evolution. Now the time has come when the mysteries must be rediscovered. They must be rediscovered. One must be fully aware of this—that today a new approach must begin to rediscovering the mysteries.
>
> This awareness provided the impetus for the Christmas Foundation Meeting: it is urgently necessary for there to be a place on earth where mysteries can once again be founded. As it continues and develops, the Anthroposophical Society must become the path towards the renewed mysteries.[112]

*

Immediately in 1923, the year following the burning of the Goetheanum, and in preparation for the forthcoming refounding of the Society, Rudolf Steiner stepped up his lecturing activity. Lindenberg writes:

> ...as if to compensate for loss of the building by still more concentrated work, during this year Rudolf Steiner intensifies his expansive and strikingly pictorial accounts of spiritual connections. In place of the building which has now vanished from visibility come the cosmic imaginations whose luminosity, especially in the lectures of autumn 1923, shine forth in a way that cannot be ignored.[113]

The wooden building of the first Goetheanum, its portrayal of the history of creation and of the human being—as outlined in *Occult Science*—was destroyed by fire in the night of New Year 1922/23. In the wake of this death experience, for the Easter festival of resurrection, Rudolf Steiner gave great and vivid accounts whose theme was the human being's place within nature and the cosmos, within the changing seasons and their substance-related secrets. Between 31 March and 8 April 1923, in five wide-ranging lectures given at the joinery workshop in Dornach, Steiner spoke of 'The cycle of the year as breathing process of the earth' and of the four major festivals. Then, six months later, at Michaelmas, Steiner continued and deepened these themes in Vienna, Dornach and Stuttgart. In August 1923, Ita Wegman—who was in Steiner's intimate proximity since the fire and spoke with him about many spiritual matters—asked about a renewal of the mysteries in relation to Christian esoteric schooling and in relation to a new mystery centre for humanity which could emanate a healing effect for all areas of civilization. Wegman asked her question at Penmaenmawr, an ancient landscape which—according to Steiner—revealed an 'elemental esoteric mood'. As Rudolf Steiner later said, her question was the

basis and precondition for the Christmas Foundation event—
for the new founding of the Dornach School as an 'esoteric
institution'.[114]

Guenther Wachsmuth, who had nearly finished his book
on formative forces, was also present at Penmaenmawr.
Rudolf Steiner climbed up with him to a plateau to visit stone
circles that were related to Druid mysteries of ancient times:

> Despite his 62 years, he climbed swiftly up the slope in
> sprightly fashion. In harmony with the spiritual atmo-
> sphere of the place, our conversation focused on the Druid
> mysteries and their counterpole in Europe, that of Mithras
> worship, as contrast of southern and northern mysteries.
> [...] Climbing persistently and tirelessly, Rudolf Steiner
> [...] explained to me the great antithesis between the Druid
> and Mithras cults, the northern and southern mysteries of
> Europe; and how the northern spiritual stream, radiating
> from Ireland, encountered the southern stream in Central
> Europe, as could be seen from the mystery sites in the
> Danube region also, and how then both found their destiny
> in the rise of Christianity. When we arrived at the crag high
> above Penmaenmawr, we could now see the lonely circle of
> the plateau surrounded by peaks, at whose centre stood the
> mighty stones of the Druid circle. It was a moment in one's
> life that always remains fresh in memory, a uniquely
> strange picture, as Rudolf Steiner now stepped into the
> middle of the Druid circle amidst the loneliness of this high
> plateau. He urged me to line up my vision so that it
> extended from the circle's stones to the peaks of the
> mountains surrounding the plateau; and then described—
> with an intensity as if it was happening at this very
> moment—how the Druid priests used this sightline to focus
> on the star signs passing across the horizon throughout the

year and thus experienced the spiritual cosmos, the beings working within it, and the task they asked of human beings. He spoke of how they organized the festivals of initiation and seasonal worship according to these cosmic rhythms, and passed to members of their communities their priestly instructions; how the unfolding of the seasons had to be reflected spiritually in their acts of worship, and physically right into the way they managed agricultural work. He spoke of sun and shadow experiences in the inner stone chamber of the old initiation sites, and of how the visions and impulses received there spread abroad across the breadths of the globe.[115]

Guenther Wachsmuth no doubt understood that Rudolf Steiner's spiritual gaze backwards to ancient times was in definite and direct relation to the future, and that Steiner had good reason for talking to him about the way life was organized by initiates at ancient sites of worship, through to instructions about agricultural matters:

> ... how they organized the festivals of initiation and seasonal worship according to these cosmic rhythms, and passed to the members of their communities their priestly instructions; *how the unfolding of the seasons had to be reflected spiritually in their acts of worship, and physically right into the way they handled agricultural work.*

After his return from Penmaenmawr, Rudolf Steiner's lectures accentuated the theme of ancient and future mystery content. With the lectures on 'Mystery Centres' he gave between November and December 1923 in the Dornach joinery workshop—which focused on the teachings and initiation rites at Ephesus, Eleusis, Samothrace, Hibernia, and in the Middle Ages, before these passed over into the Rosicrucian mystery school—Steiner was spiritually preparing the Christmas Foundation Meeting. The Goetheanum with its esoteric school was to become the Michael mystery site of the future. This is what he had intended the esoteric school to be in Dornach as long ago as 1914, and now he wished, in the last phase of his life, to establish it or at least prepare the ground for it, as a *healing* focus for a world that had fallen ill:

> That is in a certain sense the prime, true impetus of the Christ impulse: healing. The Saviour, the healer: this is His especial calling in the fifth post-Atlantean epoch. [...] The natural life of human beings from the fifth post-Atlantean epoch onwards is [...] a kind of continual, slow sickening.[116]

While Rudolf Steiner gave the first lecture of the 'Mystery Centres' cycle on 23 November 1923 in Dornach, Count von Keyserlingk, at Koberwitz in Silesia, was writing his long, pre-Christmas letter to him, asking for the agriculture course to be held in January or February 1924. Four weeks later, when Keyserlingk sent his nephew Alexander to Dornach to underline his intentions, the latter found himself in a 'public mystery act' (Zeylmans van Emmichoven):

> The verses for the laying of the Foundation Stone were the most impressive event. On one occasion they lasted well into the night and whilst they were being spoken a raging storm broke out. When Rudolf Steiner was asked why this had happened he replied: 'The elemental beings were afraid that they were not being included'.[117]

*

The renewed request for an agriculture course, which arrived in Dornach in the pre-Christmas period 1923 in Count

Keyserlingk's handwriting, was in harmony with the new founding of the School and its Sections. Since the most ancient times, agriculture had belonged within the scope of mystery knowledge, originally receiving from it its rhythms and rules. The Science and Medical Sections of the School, but also the Mathematics and Astronomy Section, were in future to be concerned, also, with questions of nutrition and agriculture, in collaboration with farmers and scientists. In contrast to 1922, Rudolf Steiner was now also involved in creating the necessary organizational form for these things himself. However his schedule was full for 1924: there were mountains of work awaiting him where he was, connected with the founding of the School and the reforming of the Society, as well as the intended rebuilding of the Goetheanum. Koberwitz and Breslau were far away and this course—in Steiner's words—far off 'in the furthest corner of the East',[118] was a difficult undertaking, also as regards Rudolf Steiner's own strength. Since the Goetheanum fire, his physical state had been fragile following the many exhausting events of previous years, and crowned by the catastrophe at Dornach. To Marie Steiner and Ita Wegman, his physician, Steiner spoke of how the Goetheanum's destruction had attacked his own constitution: '"*In comparison to other people, I have really already died here on earth*", was the phrase he often used.' His etheric body, he said, had been sundered from his physical body by this attack: '...my I and my astral body are [now] directing the physical body and augmenting the etheric'.[119] It was only by the greatest effort of will that Rudolf Steiner could continue to work after the Goetheanum fire; during the second half of 1923, his weakness had grown ever more apparent, and he had difficulties eating.

Rudolf Steiner worked intensively with Ita Wegman on

developing a Medical Section at the Goetheanum with worldwide activities. Systematic schooling courses, whose esoteric orientation accorded entirely with the Christmas Foundation Meeting, had begun in this Section for a group of young medical students and physicians on 2 January 1924, immediately after the end of the Christmas Meeting.[120] Steiner and Wegman continued this work intensively, alongside joint clinical practice, developing medicines production and writing an innovative medical textbook, whose importance Rudolf Steiner repeatedly highlighted during the Christmas Foundation Meeting and in the months thereafter, although the manuscript was as yet by no means complete:

> Efforts by myself and Frau Dr Wegman will bring this [esoteric] character into medicine in the form of a publication due to appear soon which speaks frankly and freely of what occult insights can give to medicine. This is also the deepest impulse underlying [. . .] the Christmas Foundation Meeting.[121]

Ita Wegman had always included healthy nutrition for her patients as one of the foundations of a medicine extended by spiritual science, initiating many related developments, and even purchasing the Sonnenhof in Arlesheim with the aim of supplying home-produced food to the clinic. Nevertheless, she was irritated by news of the forthcoming course on agriculture, in view of the huge workload facing Rudolf Steiner and his own strength. She was also concerned about the long journey to Breslau. All other profession-specific courses for the new School took place in Dornach in 1924—all the courses for medical students and physicians, curative educators, priests, eurythmists, speech practitioners and actors. Yet now Rudolf Steiner was meant to, or wanted to travel to far-off Silesia, in his fragile state and without any additional protection. It is not known whether Ita Wegman made the (obvious) suggestion that the farmers might come to Dornach.

At the same time, during the first months after the Christmas Foundation Meeting, Rudolf Steiner's spiritual-scientific lectures in the joinery workshop at Dornach continued with full and abundant force. In mid-February Steiner opened the 'First Class', the fundamental course of the new 'esoteric school at the Goetheanum'; one day later he began to give his karma lectures, the content of which, as Steiner repeatedly hinted, was wrested from adversary forces and powers. On Good Friday, for the first time, Rudolf Steiner referred in Dornach to the need for a future festival of Michael, 'a festival of soul courage, soul strength, soul activity',[122] which, insofar as it could come to proper fruition, would signify a *'mighty impulse for civilization's continuation'*.[123] Rudolf Steiner's lectures at and after the Christmas Foundation Meeting opened up far-reaching perspectives: imbued with light and warmth, they were drawn from the esoteric core of anthroposophy. Nevertheless, Ita Wegman—like Marie Steiner also—experienced the risk of the whole situation, and the danger for Rudolf Steiner's own life in this 'forwards flight'. In Paris, where they accompanied their teacher during the last week of May for lectures which he gave there, Ita Wegman heard him say to members:

However, it is connected [with the Christmas Foundation Meeting] that there are also—I mean now from the spiritual side—very strong adversary forces, demonic forces storming against the anthroposophical movement. But we may certainly hope that the strength of the alliance we were able to conclude with good spiritual forces through the Christmas Foundation Meeting, will in future prove capable of driving away all these spiritual oppositional forces which do, after all, make use of human beings on earth to achieve their aims.[124]

Rudolf Steiner revealed further aspects of this situation to Ita Wegman, in a direct, personal way.[125] He did not, however, allow anyone—not Ita Wegman or anyone else—to persuade him to relinquish his promise to travel to Koberwitz in June.

Shortly before his departure for Silesia, Rudolf Steiner not only completed his 'archetypal plant' watercolour, but on 4 June also spoke about the 'The Whitsun Thought as Feeling Foundation for Understanding Karma'. In this lecture Steiner opened up new perspectives for understanding the cosmos, and described the super-physical nature of the universe: 'There is nothing physical out there. The physical is only on earth, and it is simply fantasy to speak of physical nature in the universe. In the universe you find the etheric, and then the astral.'[126] Rudolf Steiner also described in a way he had never done before the manifestation of the etheric in the blue of the heavens: 'The ether becomes [...] perceptible through the heaven's blue.' The world of stars is a 'door of entry' for the astral, so that 'the astral shimmers in wherever stars shimmer'. The starry heavens, he said, should really be regarded as a 'soul expression of the universal astrality': 'The stars are an expression of love, with which the astral cosmos works upon the etheric cosmos!'[127]

Steiner continues by saying that as human beings on earth we are touched by the stars' 'love workings', and can experience these 'love emanations' as a correspondingly refined and more subtle manifestation of 'human caresses', as an expression of the 'spirit-selfhood of the universe, or of the active, destiny-creating hierarchies:

If I observe a person's form, if I look at his eyes shining at me, if I hear his voice, this is how the person expresses himself. If I gaze up to the breadths of the universe, up to the stars, these are the expressions of the hierarchies, the manifestations of the feeling-kindling life of the hierarchies. If I gaze into the endless blue of the firmament of the heavens, I see an external manifestation of their etheric body, which is, however, the lowest level of this whole hierarchical world.[128]

Rudolf Steiner's lecture led finally into the sphere of the Rosicrucian verse *Ex deo nascimur / In Christo morimur / Per spiritum sanctum reviviscimus* and its connection with what, on 4 June 1924, he called the 'Christmas, Easter and Whitsun thought'. In his karma lectures and Class lessons over recent weeks, he had highlighted ever more profound and cosmic aspects of the nature of the human being and destiny, of the *Per spiritum sanctum reviviscimus*. Now, shortly before he left to give the agriculture lectures at Whitsun, he took his farewell in the Dornach joinery workshop with a remarkable Whitsun address about the cosmos—the incarnated and reincarnated human being in the light of the hierarchical universe:

And when we come together again after the trip I now need to take at Whitsun for the agriculture course, then bring with you this sense that should live on as the warm, fiery Whitsun thought, and then we will be able to speak further about karma.

In this way your understanding will be made properly fruitful by the Whitsun thought. As once, before the Whitsun festival was inaugurated, something lit up in each of the disciples at the first celebration of Whitsun, so now the Whitsun thought should really come to life again for anthroposophical insight.

Out of your souls something should grow luminous.[129]

Soon after this, Rudolf Steiner set off for Basel railway station, accompanied by Guenther Wachsmuth and Elisabeth Vreede, the leaders of the Science and Astronomy and Mathematics Sections of the new School, who were also travelling to Koberwitz. As preparatory reading, Rudolf Steiner had recommended to the farmers his account of Christology and cosmology, *Occult Science*, and the schooling book *Knowledge of Higher Worlds*. His latest Dornach lecture and transcripts of the many lectures on the seasons and the mysteries over the past 12 months would also have been relevant.

According to Johanna von Keyserlingk, Rudolf Steiner's arrival was scheduled for 9 p.m. on the evening of Friday 6 June at Breslau station, and roughly one hour later at Koberwitz—a radical change from the surroundings of the Dornach joinery workshop to a mansion in far-off Silesia:

Everything was ready to make these Whitsun days a festive occasion. Cleaning and renovating had been going on for weeks; there were still flowers to arrange and birch branches to place in the anteroom and in front of the house doors. In thankfulness, I played a chorale which rang through the house.[130]

*

When Rudolf Steiner arrived in Breslau, Johanna von Keyserlingk was not the only one surprised to see his poor state of health, in fact his altered appearance two years after they had last seen him:

I was shocked to see how wretchedly unwell the Doctor looked—quite different from his usual self. Reports had reached us from Dornach about the serious ill health of Rudolf Steiner, so that the greatest care seemed to be called for in every respect during his stay with us here in the east.[131]

'It was as though death had already engraved its insignia in him,' she also wrote.[132] The young Kurt von Wistinghausen, who was waiting in Koberwitz with his priest colleagues and the domestic staff for the arrival of Keyserlingk's car from Breslau, was likewise shaken by Rudolf Steiner's appearance:

> It was getting dark already as the car finally arrived. After he emerged from the car, we were all shocked by his extremely haggard appearance. Though it was summer, he wore a winter coat. A carrying cord attached to the handle of his heavy briefcase and thrown over his shoulder, dug deep into the dark material of his coat.[133]

Johanna von Keyserlingk wrote of her further impressions of Rudolf Steiner after his train journey, during the late evening of his arrival at Koberwitz:

> It seemed to me that the Doctor had risen in his spirit into yet higher heavenly regions and thereby greatly increased the gulf between himself and mankind. It was shattering to see him—all had the same impression.
>
> Rudolf Steiner told one or two jokes during the evening meal, to lighten the atmosphere. But things did not cheer up, even though the heartfelt wish of most of those present—to be close to Rudolf Steiner—had been fulfilled.
>
> I had asked Frau Walter, who had formerly been in the Doctor's house in Berlin for years, to relieve me of the responsibility for his personal care, so that the meals could be prepared from the recipes of the Arlesheim Clinic. I could thus rest assured that Rudolf Steiner would be looked after in this respect with the utmost care.

Graciously, but infinitely tired, he took his leave of us to go to his room.[134]

As Rudolf Steiner and Marie Steiner-von Sivers moved into their room on the mansion's first floor, the Count and Countess Keyserlingk remained behind in uncertainty. 'What had people done to him? How could such a thing have happened?'[135] All the events in Dornach, the struggle there and Rudolf Steiner's inner situation over the past two years were something the Keyserlingks had largely heard about only from a distance; but, with only a few exceptions, even people at the Goetheanum did not know much about it. These few exceptions included Rudolf Steiner's close collaborator on the Christ sculpture Edith Maryon, whose cremation had taken place four weeks previously, on 6 May, after her long suffering and continual worry about Rudolf Steiner's life following the destruction of the first building.[136] It is possible that on the evening of 6 June 1924, Carl and Johanna von Keyserlingk sensed the reasons for Rudolf Steiner's difficulties in committing himself to give the course at Koberwitz, and the kind of pressures he was under in his work for the anthroposophical movement.

According to Johanna von Keyserlingk, the Count established a special, round-the-clock 'guard duty' for Rudolf Steiner shortly after he arrived at Koberwitz, staffed by the woodsman and various young people. 'It seemed to us that the Doctor had made a very specific hint in this regard in the car, to warn us. We realized that we were responsible for his life.'[137]

After his arrival in Koberwitz, Rudolf Steiner's life was to last only a further ten months—and in every respect Steiner had come late to Silesia. But at the Count's residence he was safe—and the 'guard' of young people organized by Keyserlingk functioned extremely well over the next ten days: 'They carried out his instructions, kept watch and relieved each other, just like adjutants of the General Staff.'[138]

Koberwitz Mansion

3

'Glorious Whitsun Weather'

The atmosphere of the conference

What trouble have I had? I only had to travel here, and am here
under the best and most beautiful conditions. All the unpleasant
tasks are undertaken by others; I only have to speak every day,
though I confess I stood before these lectures with a certain awe—
for they enter into a new domain. My trouble after all was not
so great.
Rudolf Steiner[139]

On 7 June, the day before Whit Sunday, the sun was shining
and Rudolf Steiner was working in the early morning on the
next chapter of his *Autobiography*—awaited in Dornach by
its editor Albert Steffen—which was being published in *Das
Goetheanum* magazine. Then Rudolf Steiner held a first
meeting with representatives of the anthroposophical youth
group in Breslau—a request for which had only just reached
him. 'He immediately responded and took an interest in
working with the young people, who for the most part were
not even yet members of the Anthroposophical Society.'[140]
At close to 8.30 a.m., Rudolf Steiner and Count von Keyserlingk stood waiting for over 130 course participants who
were arriving from Breslau on the morning train:[141] these
were estate owners and leasers, gardeners and people working
in agriculture, as well as committed and interested people. In
front of the mansion's main entrance Carl von Keyserlingk
introduced Rudolf Steiner personally to each participant,
amidst a great coming and going: 'The firm's transport was

used and the whole house was full. Servants, chauffeurs and gardeners were in uniform and all were given their duties.'[142]

Carl von Keyserlingk had been strict about who he admitted to the course—only anthroposophists working in agriculture were allowed to attend, in line with the prior intention of a profession-specific and protected teaching course. However Rudolf Steiner allowed numerous exceptions at the gateway of Koberwitz Mansion; he made individual decisions—something that always characterized his relations with rules and people, based on their individual personalities and life paths. When 27-year-old Wilhelm Rath appeared outside Koberwitz mansion (he had studied German literature and directed anthroposophical student work in Berlin) to hand Steiner a letter from Walter Johannes Stein from Stuttgart, just such a situation arose. Rath had travelled from Stuttgart to Breslau the evening before, for the youth meeting they hoped to have with Rudolf Steiner:

When I arrived late in the evening in Breslau, I straight-away asked where Dr Steiner was staying. I was told that it was at Koberwitz with Count Keyserlingk. I decided to go there next day by the first train.

When I arrived at the little station it struck me that a lot of people were alighting there. I followed them to the beautiful house standing in a great park. When all had gone into the house, Dr Wachsmuth was still standing by the front door. I asked him if this was where Dr Steiner was staying. He confirmed it, but added: 'But what is about to take place here is only for farmers!'

At that moment I noticed Rudolf Steiner coming down the stairs. I went up to him and handed him the fat letter with greetings from Dr Stein. Herr Doktor took it in both hands as though he was expecting me to say something. So

I plucked up the courage to say that as I had got here, and although Dr Wachsmuth had told me that the lecture was only for farmers, I would like to ask him if I could attend without being a farmer. Rudolf Steiner's eyes lit up and he said merrily: 'Well if you're not a *Landwirt* [farmer], at least you may be a *Landstreicher* [vagrant]!' Then he put his hand on my shoulder, and guided me into the room like that past Dr Wachsmuth, saying to the latter: 'We will give him a ticket, don't you think?' So I sat down among the farmers, received my ticket and was able to attend all the lectures of the agricultural course. That was of decisive importance for my entire life.[143]

Later Rudolf Steiner spoke of the 'admirable tolerance' of the farmers—or of Count Keyserlingk—which had allowed some additional people to attend. Rudolf Steiner himself had dismissed others:

There was a gentleman who had been hanging around on the fringes of anthroposophy for years without getting properly involved. He wished to attend the agricultural lectures with his wife, who was a participant. Not being allowed to attend, he was forced to return home. Rudolf Steiner did not sanction such external interest, of the kind that just finds something 'interesting'.[144]

*

On Saturday, the day before Whitsun, Koberwitz Mansion was decorated with flowers and was to remain so for the next 11 days. Rudolf Steiner's lectures took place in the mansion's large dining room, extended into the vestibule by opening the double doors. Steiner was surrounded by 130 chairs as he spoke, and stood at a lectern in the middle of the room, with a board and easel close by.

On Saturday morning, however, Carl von Keyserlingk first stood up to speak, offering profound thanks for Rudolf Steiner's presence, and apologizing for the bad night which the eurythmists in Marie Steiner's troupe had spent in Breslau hotels (Marie Steiner had received complaints about bed bugs in the hotel the following morning): 'My husband said he was sorry that they had been welcomed to Silesia by small creatures, which was unfortunately unavoidable. Even Goethe, he said, described such a welcome when he came here.'[145]

Then Rudolf Steiner welcomed the guests and spoke of the *'thanks of Anthroposophia herself—thanks which in these hard times are due to all who share in anthroposophical interests'*.[146] He went on to say about Koberwitz, his arrival, and the fact that the course was being held there:

> Indeed, it is deeply gratifying that we are able to hold this agriculture course here in the house of Count and Countess Keyserlingk. I know from my former visits what a beautiful atmosphere there is in Koberwitz—I mean especially the spiritual atmosphere. I know that the atmosphere of soul and spirit which is living here is the best possible basis for what must be said during this course [...] it seems to me we could scarcely be accommodated better for this lecture course than here, in a farm so excellent and so exemplary.[147]

Rudolf Steiner thanked Carl von Keyserlingk in person—for his commitment in preparing and organizing the conference that was now starting, and indeed for all his efforts on behalf of a new agriculture extended through anthroposophical spiritual science:

> Was it not Count Keyserlingk who helped us from the very outset with his advice and his devoted work, in the farming

activities we undertook at Stuttgart as part of the company Der Kommende Tag? His spirit, trained by his deep and intimate connection with agriculture, was active in all that we were able to do in this direction. And I would say that forces prevailed which came from the inmost heart of our movement and which drew us hither, quite as a matter of course, the moment the Count desired us to come to Koberwitz.[148]

Rudolf Steiner gave the impression of being pleased to be at Koberwitz at last, despite all the efforts and difficulties that lay behind him. He spoke of the 'feeling environment' necessary for anthroposophy—and that now festive and work days would follow ('*I trust they will also be days of truly good work here in this house*'). At the end of his words of welcome, Rudolf Steiner said that the results and even the form of the course remained open for him in a certain sense, and a little later stated: 'I do not know whether the things which can be said at this stage out of anthroposophy will satisfy you in every respect, but I will do my best to explain what anthroposophy can give for agriculture.'[149]

Three days later Rudolf Steiner wrote to Ita Wegman to say that he had approached the agricultural lectures '*without all that much hope*',[150] a notable statement which shows that he himself was not entirely sure how the coming ten days would go, and was perhaps even unsure about the possible quality of what he would teach. Whether all questions could be answered adequately, and whether farmers would absorb the fundamental perspectives he offered was clearly debatable for him, not to mention the extent to which spiritual-scientific explanations might themselves be successful. Looking back later, Rudolf Steiner said that he had '*considerable respect*' in relation to the agriculture lectures, '*since they are a new area*'.[151] Whether his delay in arriving at Koberwitz might—alongside everything else—also have been connected with this fact, is unclear. Immediately after his words of greeting, however, Rudolf Steiner proceeded to give his first lecture on fundamental aspects of agriculture.

*

Following Rudolf Steiner's first lecture—as after all other course lectures—an extensive second breakfast was laid on for all participants, with 600 prepared sandwiches to be eaten while standing and walking about ('The woodsman sliced the bread, the chauffeur sliced the cheese and sausage'[152]). For Rudolf Steiner himself, a facility to withdraw and rest was made available:

> We were a little uncertain what we should do. We thought Herr Doktor would wish to rest after his lecture, for he looked tired; and we therefore laid a breakfast for him, Frau Doktor and Fräulein Vreede in a separate room. But I don't think he really liked that: he preferred to be with everyone.[153]

In the following days, indeed, Rudolf Steiner always remained amongst the breakfasting guests after his lecture: 'In the break all conversed together in lively discussions, and Dr Steiner passed amongst us very cheerfully.'[154] And:

> When [...] we, the audience, went outdoors in front of the mansion during breakfast, and, with our small breakfast plates in hand, enjoyed the glorious Whitsun weather beneath the trees of the park, Rudolf Steiner accompanied us, available for anyone to speak with, so simple and unpretentious that no one gave any thought to the fact that the mantle of Elijah hung upon his shoulders.[155]

Already on the first afternoon of his stay at Koberwitz, Rudolf Steiner wrote to Ita Wegman in Arlesheim to tell her he was physically well: '*I am profoundly happy that I feel well, and can tell you that I coped well with the journey too. I hope nothing bad will occur.*'[156]

Rudolf Steiner had arrived at Koberwitz unwell, and after his first lecture looked 'tired'. But the subsequent days and the whole atmosphere of the conference did him good. The generous scope of the mansion and its inhabitants, the glorious, warm Whitsun sun, the life-focused theme he was speaking on, and the etheric level of his own lectures—to and amidst practising farmers—clearly gave him additional strength. Later Johanna von Keyserlingk remarked that '. . . he seemed to give the lectures with great pleasure and looked quite youthful. From day to day he looked better in health and more cheerful, and his health and good spirits spread confidence and happiness over all who were present.'[157] The preparation of Rudolf Steiner's food, too, which had caused a good deal of prior concern, ran smoothly from the outset:

Every lunchtime he was given an excellent soup prepared from vegetables, herbs, cheese and caraway; then two soft-boiled eggs which Frau Walter herself collected from the hens to make sure they were fresh, and an Austrian dessert. Herr Doktor always ate everything he was given: he seemed to find it tasty, but it was also prepared with such love and care. On one occasion I was very surprised to see that he wasn't eating the soup, and I asked him why. 'Because I have no spoon' he answered laconically; and laughing we brought him one. With every day that passed Herr Doktor looked more cheerful and healthier, so that our worries about him from the first day or so soon seemed a thing of the past.[158]

But those in his more intimate circle knew that such worries were justified, and Rudolf Steiner was never euphoric in his letters from Koberwitz to Ita Wegman: 'I am trying to keep my health on an even keel here—at present I have nothing unfavourable to report' (10 June[159]). 'My health will hold up' (12 June[160]). Nevertheless, one could not help noticing that Rudolf Steiner was recovering somewhat at Koberwitz, and that the theme of his lectures did him good:

> How warmly and knowledgeably he spoke, for instance, about the way to build a compost heap! One was immediately transported to a farm setting and had to believe that this was his real profession, in which he felt at home. It seemed to be quite natural when Count Keyserlingk afterwards addressed Rudolf Steiner on behalf of the assembled landowners, farm-workers and gardeners as the 'great peasant' from whom everyone would gladly take instruction for their profession.[161]

Those fortunate enough to experience the agriculture course, and especially Steiner's accounts of practical measures—of crops, cattle and manure—also experienced the extraordinary sense of spiritual sacrament that imbued everything. Gravity and humour were uniquely allied. Dr Steiner related to the assembled participants, to individuals and to the hosts, Count and Countess Keyserlingk, with an incomparable and unforgettable dignity. (Kurt von Wistinghausen[162])

*

On the morning of Whitsun, Rudolf Steiner took a detailed tour round the estate. Accompanied by the Count and Countess Keyserlingk, at his own request he walked to the gardens and vegetable beds ('Herr Doktor told Carl that he wished to see the farm, estate and park this morning'[163]).

Although this was not his first stay at Koberwitz, he had never before inspected the estate as such. Now Steiner made a series of observations and remarks, among other things concerning the high iron content of the soil, which he also reported to Ita Wegman in a letter a few hours later, on the early afternoon of Whit Sunday:

> This morning I inspected the vegetable beds, the farm and the livestock at Koberwitz. It was all very interesting. I'm surprised by the water, which has a high iron content. And I started to consider how this water, whose iron is even apparent as residue in the washbasins, might be used medicinally. I believe it might be put to very valuable use.[164]

Johanna von Keyserlingk wrote as follows about Rudolf Steiner's remarks on the iron in the estate gardens:

> Dr Steiner said that one could tell from the roses and also the lettuce that they did not feel happy in this iron-rich soil. Carl replied that everything here was so permeated with iron and that was why the water was almost undrinkable. Herr Doktor said he would like to have a look at the water. While the park keeper was fetched—whose job it was to operate the pumps—Herr Doktor went over to the roses once again to examine their sorry state. 'Yes,' he said, 'your roses will not thrive in this iron-rich soil. You'd need to introduce other soil here, or add a lead dilution to neutralize the iron.'
>
> In the meantime the pump house had been opened and Herr Doktor now tasted the water. Frau Doktor was rather appalled at this, because of his ailing stomach. Smiling, he said that the water could certainly serve as a curative drink for gall complaints.

Herr Doktor then returned to the house accompanied by Carl and myself, saying something to us which first struck us as odd—that the iron in this soil had a connection with us, and it was with good reason that he had referred to the 'iron Count and Countess' yesterday. 'You both have an iron will, as far as pursuing your goals is concerned; and there really is a connection—these things attract one another.' We only slowly understood what he meant.[165]

In looking back to his time in Koberwitz and the character of the Count and Countess, Rudolf Steiner commented in Dornach after his return: 'There was indeed something iron-like in their bearing.'[166] In his joinery workshop lecture on 'The Michael Imagination' on 5 October 1923, he spoke extensively about the mysteries of the iron process—in connection with observations on a future festival of Michael. There Rudolf Steiner identified 'freeing oneself from anxiety and fear' as physiological motifs of the effects of iron on the blood, saying among other things:

[The human being] must learn to celebrate the festival of Michael by creating the Michael festival as one which dispels fear—a festival of fearlessness, a festival of inner initiative and inner strength—by making the Michael festival into a recalling of selfless self-awareness.[167]

It was Whitsun, not autumn, when Rudolf Steiner walked around the Koberwitz estate—a radiant, warm Sunday morning in June. Yet Carl von Keyserlingk had made the course happen, made it possible through such 'selfless self-awareness', without fuss and against all obstacles, through difficult times for the estates company Vom Rath, Schöller and Skene AG and through dark times at Dornach and in Central Europe. And Rudolf Steiner was profoundly thankful to him for this. Now, at Koberwitz, something new and 'Michaelic' could begin, and in the coming days was to assume ever clearer form.

*

Johanna von Keyserlingk wrote as follows about the further tour of the estate on that Whitsun morning:

> Close by the woodsman's house I called our lovely brown setter to show him to Herr Doktor, who wanted to greet him, but the dog held back warily. I said I thought it was out of shyness, but Herr Doktor said it was because the dog had been thrashed. Then I passed my new orchard with him, which wasn't growing very well, probably because it was situated too low down, and was damp. He mentioned that potassium-manganese should be used in such cases.
>
> From the lake, happy laughter floated over from where the eurythmists were boating. Herr Doktor loved them as though they were all his own children.[168]

According to Johanna von Keyserlingk, directly after the walk Rudolf Steiner gave an esoteric class to a small group in the mansion, in the late morning of Whit Sunday:

> Rudolf Steiner spoke about meditations which the farmer should address to himself and his earth, and about beings which descend into the community of a farm and are active in the earth, the plants and the farm surroundings—and how then it would be possible for people to influence the weather by means of their moral will forces. He spoke urgently about the degeneration of foodstuffs and how necessary it is to cultivate new plants. He also said that a whole new science should be established which would be effective not in isolation but through esoteric realities. [. . .]

He spoke about angel choirs which congregate above the places where people form communities, to prepare for the instreaming of exalted spiritual beings willing to help mankind. By forming such communities one would be able to exert a healing influence on the life of plants. And Rudolf Steiner added, with a friendly glance towards Frau Dr Vreede: 'And it is Dr Vreede who will bring about this connection to the spirits of the spheres through her work.'[169]

Five months previously, on 5 January 1924, the day before Epiphany, Rudolf Steiner had given the group of 'young doctors' a first meditation during their medical course in the Glass House at Dornach ('The ethics of medical study and practice [esoteric and exoteric]'). This was an exercise to promote inner engagement with the formative principles and spiritual environment of plants, with a subsequent address to the human I and the will path towards self-transformation:

Spirits of healing,
you unite
with the blessed sulphur
of ethereal fragrance.

You invigorate yourselves
in Mercury's upward striving
in the drop of dew
in what grows
and develops.

You come to a halt
in the salt of earth
that nourishes the root
in the soil.

I seek to unite
my soul's wisdom with the fire
of blossom's fragrance;

I seek to enliven my life of soul
through the glittering drop
of the leaves of morning;

I seek to strengthen my soul existence
through the salt-hardening force
with which the earth
carefully tends the root.[170]

*

According to Countess Keyserlingk, in his esoteric Whitsun address, too, Rudolf Steiner said that spiritual-scientific insights could only be disseminated through the *Johannine Word*, which accorded with the universal Word, the Logos. In contrast, all approach to such insights from the standpoint of modern, materialistic science would, he said, harm their esoteric content, and even sunder them from the cooperative activity of the Logos.[171]

A week later, in the early morning of Sunday 15 June—when Rudolf Steiner's autobiographical essay about his first preoccupation with Goethe's fairytale 'The Green Snake and the Beautiful Lily' appeared in the Dornach weekly *Das Goetheanum*—a further esoteric class 'relating to the agricultural lectures' was, according to Countess Keyserlingk, held in the mansion at the suggestion of Ernst Stegemann. 'Only a few people attended, only the older Class members.'[172] Johanna von Keyserlingk related nothing about the contents of this second class; it is possible, however, that Rudolf Steiner gave further suggestions there about ways of living esoterically with the content of the agricultural lectures.

The same day, 15 June, the penultimate day of the course, Rudolf Steiner gave the three participating priests of The Christian Community the text of the St John epistles, which he had written down the previous night:

It was during a break in the agricultural lectures in Koberwitz that Rudolf Steiner approached us and quite simply, but with inner joy himself at such a text, handed us a paper on which was the ritual of the new St John's Service, which he had completed that night. (Rudolf Meyer)[173]

We immediately read the texts together in the park, and Dr Steiner asked us subsequently whether we liked them. We pointed out a spelling mistake, which he most gladly corrected straight away. (Kurt von Wistinghausen)[174]

Nine days later was St John's day—and the epistles were spoken as part of the Act of Consecration of Man service. As in the ancient culmination times of mystery cultures, initiation deeds were combined at Koberwitz: Rudolf Steiner was teaching the farmers about the spiritual dimensions of their work. At the same time he initiated an act of worship, in the same way as he had described this to Guenther Wachsmuth in relation to ancient times, when they viewed the Druid stones together ('He related how they organized the festivals of initiation and seasonal worship according to these cosmic rhythms, and passed to the members of their communities their priestly instructions; how the unfolding of the seasons had to be reflected spiritually in their acts of worship, and physically right into the way they handled agricultural work.')

*

After the opening lecture on Saturday 7 June, and the pause over the two Whitsun festival days, Rudolf Steiner's agricultural lectures took place each morning from 10 to 16 June over seven consecutive days (Monday through to Monday). After the breakfast breaks, extensive question and answer sessions were held with Rudolf Steiner on agricultural matters. Each afternoon, after the course participants had returned to Breslau by train, Steiner saw members of the Anthroposophical Society who wished to hold personal conversations with him at Koberwitz (and had applied to do so in advance, by letter to Count Keyserlingk). He also repeatedly saw patients, who were introduced to him in the mansion by Dr Ludwig Engel, a member of the 'young doctors' group. Prior to the conference, Count Keyserlingk had already tried to protect Rudolf Steiner from all such enquiries: '[...] Count Keyserlingk, who felt responsible for the conference, had made it clear to everyone that he would ensure that no one was to approach Rudolf Steiner with personal requests, for the latter was not well, and far too busy to cope with personal audiences alongside his lectures.'[175] Dr Engel, whom Keyserlingk also did not want to admit to the agricultural lectures, had turned to Ita Wegman seeking permission and asked her to support his request to attend the agriculture course and the patient consultations: 'If you, dear Frau Doktor, believe that this is possible, do please write to me to say so.'[176] We do not know whether Ludwig Engel received a reply from Ita Wegman before the course began. But Rudolf Steiner, with whom Ita Wegman had spoken, saw Ludwig Engel, with his red hair, outside the mansion on the morning of the first agriculture lecture, in the group of people arriving from Breslau:

We got out at the small station and made our way to the mansion. Count Keyserlingk was at the door introducing Rudolf Steiner to those who were attending the course.

Rudolf Steiner caught sight of me, beckoned me to him and said: 'Frau Dr Steiner is suffering from a weakness of the vocal cords and has to give a speech course. Can you obtain some Pyrites 3x for me?' It was not such a simple matter at that time, for pharmacists had no stocks of remedies from the 'International Laboratories'—and the post took a very long time. But I had just ordered this remedy in Stuttgart and it had arrived that morning. How glad I was to be of use so promptly! Looking in my direction he continued: 'I heard that you wanted to present some of your patients to me, but that Count Keyserlingk has raised some difficulties. Well, if the Count will not allow it, I shall simply come to you in Breslau.'

'There is no question of that, Herr Doktor,' I called out, 'Count Keyserlingk only wants to protect you from overstraining yourself! If you explain to him that you would like to see my patients, I am sure he would agree and have it arranged!' And that's how it happened.[177]

In the end, Ludwig Engel presented more than 20 of his patients to Rudolf Steiner[178]—and Steiner was very pleased with his anthroposophical medical work: 'The whole afternoon, Dr Engel was there with his patients. It is excellent how he works entirely in keeping with our ideas. I will tell you about it,' he wrote to Ita Wegman on 11 June.[179] The patients introduced to Rudolf Steiner also included Engel's own child, a small, two-year-old boy who suffered from rickets. Ludwig Engel later described this therapeutic encounter as follows:

The treatment which Rudolf Steiner described soon led to a complete recovery. While I was holding the child in my arms I noticed how Rudolf Steiner touched his head with his [Steiner's] fingers. I thought he wanted to discover if the fontanelle was still open. I saw how he made certain signs with his hand on the child's head during which his glance was turned completely inwards. I was amazed. It looked as though he was giving the boy his blessing.

*

Every evening Rudolf Steiner held his karma lectures in Breslau, accompanied on two days by Class lessons, and returned to Koberwitz in Keyserlingk's car at 11 p.m., nearly an hour's drive. Steiner embarked on his karma lectures the day after his arrival. Here is Johanna von Keyserlingk's description of his return from Breslau on this first evening and the situation at the mansion:

> Late in the evening when the cars had returned to Kober-witz, supper had been laid for Dr and Frau Steiner in their room, for them to eat alone. We others sat down together in the dining room downstairs and each quickly got some bread and butter for himself without any ceremony—then Rudolf Steiner came downstairs and told us that he did not wish to eat upstairs on his own and that he was not a prisoner. Then he put us all in a happy mood with his jokes. Someone ran to fetch his meal and we sat together with him for a happy hour around the dining table. It seemed that he had become more cheerful.[181]

This late, shared meal was repeated every evening thereafter, in the hour before midnight.

While the others went to bed exhausted, Rudolf Steiner continued to work for hours: 'Rudolf Steiner slept very little. The bedroom was so arranged that a large table was drawn up to the bedside, on which books and papers could be placed.'[182] During the nights at Koberwitz Rudolf Steiner wrote his autobiographical articles for *Das Goetheanum* magazine, spiritual-scientific essays for the members of the

Anthroposophical Society (which were published in the *Nachrichtenblatt* [newsletter]), special letters to Ita Wegman[183]—and more besides. His urgent letters were taken to the post at Breslau just before 5 a.m. each morning by Andreas von Grunelius, to whom they were passed by Alexander von Keyserlingk:

> I heard that Rudolf Steiner often worked for hours into the night after the lectures, then walked through the silent, spacious house, descended the stairs, opened the front door and handed his letters for posting to Herr Grunelius, who was waiting in his car to catch the early post train with them. So I told Rudolf Steiner that, since he went to bed so late and was first up in the morning, he ought not to have to walk through the whole house as well in the middle of the night. I would in future collect his letters. He said to me: 'But you too need your sleep!' I told him it was more important for him to get some sleep. He answered with neither a yea or nay, and so I knocked on his door at about half past three in the morning. On his 'Come in', I entered the room and saw him sitting up in bed writing. He only said: 'It will still take a few moments.' On returning some minutes later he had finished the letters and gave them to me. I did the same thing every morning.[184]

*

Rudolf Steiner scarcely had a break during the day. The servant girl Paula Eckhardt remembered him thus: 'If he was left in peace he would work in his room and never emerge. Modest he was!'[185] Steiner coped with the extra Class lessons and youth gatherings as with everything else, and attended the eurythmy performance at the Lobe Theatre on 9 June, and likewise the performance of Goethe's *Iphigenia* by the

Kugelmann players in Breslau on 15 June. Pleased and surprised by the performance, he responded by agreeing to hold a 'drama course' in the summer.

Even the late lunches after the agricultural discussions became social events for the alternating group of 12 people who were invited into the 'intimate circle' at Rudolf Steiner's table. When asked, Steiner told stories from his life, but also urged others to do the same:

> The priest, Rudolf von Koschützki, was once prompted to tell about his railway accident, from which he miraculously escaped with injuries after having been wedged under train-wreckage all night without losing consciousness.
>
> He was sitting at the table between Guenther Wachsmuth and me, and thus I was able to study from close at hand the deeply serious face of Rudolf Steiner, who looked at the speaker in silence the whole time. One could see by his countenance that he took in more of what had happened than the description of this event could express.[186]

People sitting near Rudolf Steiner at mealtimes often asked him questions, to which he willingly replied. Such questions were on the most varied themes and often led to surprising statements:

> Once, when there were strawberries for dessert, I asked him if it were really right to cultivate strawberries to such a size and he replied that under certain circumstances strawberries could die out altogether through such a practice, because it disturbed the aura of the [strawberry] group soul.[187]

On the last day of his stay at Koberwitz, Rudolf Steiner responded as follows to questions by Count Keyserlingk about Central Europe's future:

During a private conversation with Carl it was said that people did not take sufficient note of what was happening in the East. It was there that Europe's fate would be decided, for Germany would someday be only an American colony. [...]

Carl had asked Rudolf Steiner what he foresaw would be Germany's future, and the latter replied: 'The [factory] chimneys will topple and Germany will be reduced to an agrarian state.' Then Rudolf Steiner said very seriously: 'All will depend on forming islands of monastic seclusion in the countryside where German cultural and spiritual life can be cultivated. Foreign lands will send their sons and daughters there to be educated.' After a pause he added: 'And it will be a long way from one island to the next.'

Rudolf Meyer noted this conversation in roughly the following way: Germany has ceased to be of political importance. It will be reduced to an agrarian state in which oases of spiritual life will be able to exist. Then anthroposophy will have to proliferate everywhere throughout Central Europe. And it will be capable of that. Germany could acquire a mission like Greece after its suppression by Rome—as the spiritual teacher of the dominant race. It only has to recognize its task, otherwise Europe will sink into utter barbarity, and culture will die.[188]

In the same context Rudolf Steiner also said: 'The chimneys in Germany will topple. This is also just and right in terms of cosmic incarnation, for industry has put forth more toxic shoots here than anywhere else.'[189] The following night Rudolf Steiner entered into connection with the individuality of Helmuth von Moltke, the former Chief of General Staff of the German army, who had died eight years before. In the morning he gave Carl von Keyserlingk the transcript of this spiritual perception for Eliza von Moltke.[190]

*

On Friday 13 June, after a brief meal between the second Class lesson in Breslau (at 6 p.m.) and the karma lecture he gave at 8 p.m., Rudolf Steiner took advantage of a rare pause in his schedule to visit the churches on Breslau's cathedral island. There he drew the attention of those accompanying him to various things: 'He gave interesting explanations, pointing out to Wachsmuth the eye of God in a triangle positioned in the centre of the sun, and saying that people used to know a great deal about this.' However he also spent a long while alone before an altar:

> Herr Doktor stood for a long time in contemplation before the altar [of the Sandkirche] and allowed it to impress itself upon him; it was as though he was absorbing the spirituality of the atmosphere.[191]

Steiner did not even object to the general desire, on the evening of Monday 16 June, after the last course lecture had been given and the last patient consultations had taken place, to gather for concluding 'celebrations' with 370 people in a restaurant on Sand island in the centre of this town on the Oder river. Here there were addresses and artistic performances, as well as food supplied by Koberwitz estate. In his own speech, Rudolf Steiner again thanked Count Keyserlingk for all that he had accomplished—and Moritz Bartsch for his anthroposophical work in Silesia. Bartsch found it hard to accept these words of thanks from the great teacher. Years previously he had already tried to dismiss all such efforts on Steiner's part:

Rudolf Steiner tried to thank me for my anthroposophical work in Silesia, when we were sitting alone together at table on one occasion. 'But Herr Doktor,' I interrupted, 'why are you thanking me? Just take a look at me: I am only 4 ft 6 in, I ran about everywhere barefoot as a boy and climbed trees, and now I have the great good fortune to proclaim Christianity to people in a new way, in the age of the consciousness soul. This great fortune I owe to you, Herr Doktor!' He stretched out his hand to me wordlessly at this, but I believe I saw that his eyes were moist.[192]

Rudolf Steiner was profoundly grateful to the people who committed themselves to anthroposophy in the twentieth century—and he loved the humble, combative rector from Breslau, whose sons had helped prepare the agricultural course and made it possible.

In the restaurant on the island in the Oder, Rudolf Steiner again engaged in numerous conversations and seemed cheerful and happy. Ailing people also again found their way to him: 'Many had come to ask him for advice, among them a blind lady, and I can still see Rudolf Steiner's gesture as he took her groping hands lovingly in his clasp.'[193] The doctor Ludwig Engel also however later wrote:

[. . .] But Rudolf Steiner was visibly strained by the turmoil. His hair fell across his brow, upon which pearls of sweat could be seen.

Just previous to that I had been having a consultation with a lady patient, who had an eye removed some years before. Now some unpleasant symptoms were showing in the other eye. I considered her condition so serious that I told her I would try to arrange a short consultation with Dr Steiner during the festivities. I managed to do this, and Rudolf Steiner gave her some immediate advice. Not content with that, however, the lady now pulled out a sketch book: 'Here are some paintings by a medium in a trance and Herr Doktor should kindly look at them.' With obvious reluctance Rudolf Steiner turned over a few pages—he had no comment to make and appeared to be completely exhausted. Then an anxious father came and addressed himself to me. His little son had cystitis and a high temperature—what could Dr Steiner advise? With that he turned directly to Rudolf Steiner and I heard the latter say: 'Apply hot poultices with . . .' For a moment the exhausted Doctor could not find the word—'. . . with linseed'.

I felt deeply ashamed that we had exploited Rudolf Steiner to the absolute limit.[194]

In his subsequent account of this convivial evening, Rudolf Steiner made no mention of his own exhaustion but instead praised anthroposophists' appetites: '. . . all seemed to have exceptionally good appetites . . . But the nicest thing about it was that there was plenty to go around, and even a lot left over, in spite of the presence of 370 hungry anthroposophists . . .'[195] The priest and farmer Rudolf von Koschützki recorded the late conclusion of the evening of 16 June as follows:

[. . .] It was already nearly 11 and [. . .] the cars were waiting outside when a young man engaged Rudolf Steiner in conversation. Rudolf Steiner was leaning his elbow on the table and listening attentively to the young man, with his hand to his ear. But since he seemed to go on and on talking, I came up behind Rudolf Steiner's chair, pointed to my watch and tried to make the young man see that he should stop. He did not allow this to disturb him, however, and Rudolf Steiner's patience was great, and perhaps also his interest—which he showed everyone; and so we had to let things take their course.

At last we did find ourselves back at Koberwitz, though, at the long dining table; and at its head, after a tiring day, Rudolf Steiner refreshed the whole company with laughter at his cheerful anecdotes. After midnight he went to his room, whose window we could see from the wing where we were staying, and thus knew that, as ever, he was working through the night. But he said that this agricultural conference had been a celebratory event for him [...][196]

Guenther Wachsmuth wrote in similar vein of Rudolf Steiner's appearance and the social nature of his stay at Koberwitz and Breslau, speaking of the atmosphere of the whole Whitsun conference which he engendered:

Between the lectures and agricultural visits, in personal interactions, during the evening journeys [...] to Breslau for the artistic events, during the celebratory gatherings dedicated to the esoteric core of the work, and in the most varied conversations, both grave and cheerful, held within the spiritually cultivated sphere of the mansion, one could experience in the purest and most refined form Rudolf Steiner's community-building art of life: its intimacy, warm openness to colleagues, and the deed-engendering power which emanated from those moments.[197]

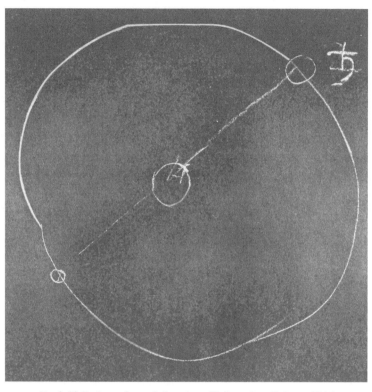

Rudolf Steiner: board drawing. Koberwitz, 7 June 1924
(Rudolf Steiner Archive)

4

The Mysteries of Agriculture

Motifs of the course

The agricultural lectures seem successful to me so far. I approached them with little hope. But now it is proving possible, here too specifically, to draw perspectives from the world of spirit which may be of the greatest fruitfulness for practical agriculture. As far as I can see, the farmers are actually absorbing these things, although they are really very much at odds with the prevailing outlook.

Rudolf Steiner to Ita Wegman
Koberwitz, 10 June 1924[198]

The eight lectures which started each morning at 11 a.m. at Koberwitz Mansion and whose aim was to 'seek spiritual-scientific methods' for agriculture,[199] were a striking and in some respects a daily intensifying event. Rudolf Steiner began slowly on the first morning, albeit from the very core of his founding ideas, and spoke about the conditions for plant growth between earthly and cosmic forces, the significance of substances—as paths to facilitate the workings of cosmic forces—and about participating planetary forces. In subsequent lectures he repeatedly accentuated the fact that anthroposophy's task was to 'look at life's wider context',[200] seeking and conveying insight into the broader workings of life. With the fading of 'instinctive agricultural wisdom'— emanating from ancient (mystery) knowledge and sustained by traditions passed on through the generations—and the rise of a modern, materialistic and causal view of nature, the more subtle, interconnected and hidden ways of nature had been increasingly banished from awareness and from agricultural practices. According to Steiner, the significance of anthroposophy does not lie in applying certain new substances, methods and procedures, but in fundamentally re-establishing a real knowledge of nature and a capacity to engage with it—with central inclusion of cosmic forces which facilitate and determine life on earth: 'Nature and the working of the spirit throughout nature must be recognized in a large, all-embracing dimension.'[201] Steiner states that a true mode of spiritual-scientific observation of agricultural themes and questions is essentially and primarily a 'study of the macrocosm'.[202] However far removed such an approach might be from modern ideas of narrowly delimited and 'circumscribed things', it is, he says, absolutely necessary for those working in agriculture, whose sphere of work is indisputably related to both the earth and the cosmos. Rudolf Steiner's audience at Koberwitz was composed of anthroposophists who had read his basic texts including his cosmological work *Occult Science*. Steiner, when asked, referred to the importance of this volume in preparation for the course. But the anthroposophically oriented farmers were nevertheless also twentieth century people, and largely alienated from a sense of macrocosmic influences and their differentiated entities. At Koberwitz, from the beginning of his first lecture, Rudolf Steiner now proceeded to open up this sphere of influence and relate it to the conditions underpinning agriculture, in a new and differentiated way, saying in explanation (although not in excuse):

So we begin really to reckon with the influences of the stars without becoming superstitious in the least. Many things later become mere superstition which were originally knowledge. Naturally you cannot warm up the old superstitions. You must make a fresh start with genuine knowledge. This knowledge however must be gained in a spiritual way—not through the mere world of physical senses.[203]

This is precisely what Immanuel Voegele had requested five months previously. At the time, Voegele had spoken to Steiner about intimations of the experiential field of various earthly and cosmic forces still available to the practising farmer but unpenetrated by conscious knowledge—which was now urgently needed:

A farmer who senses the existence of a certain inevitable relationship between human beings and the kingdoms of nature—the interaction and interpenetration of the forces of the earth, sun, stars, elementals and all other nature spirits—and who sees these interactions and interpenetrations giving rise to the mineral, plant, animal and human kingdoms, feels a host of questions assailing him at every turn in his daily work to which his current knowledge can supply no answers, and which therefore greatly trouble him as unresolved questions. *He senses the fact of these forces and their interworking, yet knows nothing of the way they do so, nor of their essential nature.*

From the first Koberwitz lecture onwards, Rudolf Steiner spoke of the 'essential nature' of 'these forces and their interworking'—in his descriptions of the outer and inner planets, their effects on silica and calcium, the 'two streams in plant development', and the cosmic facilitation of nutritional substance and generation ... At the end of his first lecture on the Saturday morning before Whitsun, Rudolf Steiner described to the assembled farmers the influence of the outer planets on trees' bark formation, drew a first illustration on the board, and, speaking of the relevance of such inter-connections in nature, their periodic cycles and of the need—also for human health—to take account of them, said:

> If someone wishes to plant an oak, it is of no little importance to have a good knowledge of the periods of Mars; for an oak, rightly planted in the proper Mars period, will thrive differently from one that is planted thoughtlessly in the earth, just when it happens to suit.
>
> Or, if you wish to plant coniferous forests, where the Saturn forces play so great a part, the result will be different if you plant the forest in a so-called ascending period of Saturn, or in some other period. One who understands can tell precisely, from the things that will grow or will not grow, whether or not they have been planted with an understanding of the context of these forces. Things which are not manifest to the external eye nevertheless appear very clearly in the more intimate circumstances of life.
>
> Assume for instance that we take, as firewood, wood that is derived from trees planted in the earth without understanding of cosmic rhythms. It will not provide the same healthy warmth as firewood from trees planted with understanding. These things enter especially into the more intimate circumstances of daily life, and it is here they show their great significance. But life has become almost void of thought for people today. They are only too glad if they do not need to think of such things.[204]

*

Rudolf Steiner did not want to 'warm up superstitions' at Koberwitz, nor did he intend to 'explain the farmers' almanac in detail, give guidelines for re-introducing it, and practical exercises for its use' which is what he had been asked to do beforehand. He was, far more radically, concerned to help people acquire a new, fundamental *knowledge,* to 'understand things fully'. In this sense the Koberwitz course was primarily a course in theory and knowledge ('You must make a fresh start with genuine knowledge'). The contents of the course grew out of work in spiritual-scientific perception and knowledge, and they aimed to help the farmer develop capacities to perceive and act autonomously. The 'instinctive wisdom' of ancient agricultural traditions was a thing of the past, which had irrevocably faded—and 'practical exercises' for using the old farmers' almanac were only of limited use in this situation:

> We, however, speaking from the point of view of anthroposophy, do not desire to return to the old instincts. We wish instead to find, out of deeper spiritual insight, what the old, now insecure instincts are less and less able to provide. To this end we must include a far wider horizon in our studies of the life of plant and animal, and of the earth itself. We must extend our view to encompass the whole cosmos.[205]

This 'deeper spiritual insight' was the living core of Rudolf Steiner's commentaries at Koberwitz, and of his whole life's work as spiritual scientist and teacher. At Koberwitz this insight related in particular to the field of nature's workings, the preconditions, conditions and developmental capacities of plant and animal life—'but we must first know how to penetrate into these wider workings of nature'.[206]

To develop insights, look into and in fact perceive and understand the forces, processes and interconnections of nature, was Rudolf Steiner's central concern in founding a new agriculture. Sensible procedures were still practised, which had developed empirically and had proven successful in all domains of agricultural work. But here too, tried and tested approaches would benefit from deeper understanding, from individual insight into and substantiation of daily practice in relation to the forces and qualities at work. As part of a longer discourse on animal feed, Rudolf Steiner said at Koberwitz:

> Much—indeed a very great deal—of what has gradually been discovered by experiment is quite correct. It is only unsystematic, lacking in precision. Precisely this kind of 'exact science' is not at all exact in reality, for many things get muddled up together *and no one can grasp them clearly* [...].[207]

In his eight Koberwitz lectures, Rudolf Steiner had no opportunity to develop a comprehensive schooling course whereby farmers could acquire new perception and knowledge of nature. He knew that they were hoping for practical suggestions and aids in coping with current problems on the land and in their stables—and, as far as he was able, he was willing to offer this help. He was also aware that the farmers' path of schooling would be accomplished through daily work, in so far as they succeeded in filling such work with new perspectives, views and insights, thus gradually deepening their practice. Steiner himself spoke in the course from direct vision, from spiritual insight. In lecture two, during a subtle description of earthly and cosmic forces at work in the plant—which he also drew on the board—he simply said: '*We see this directly.*'[208] Steiner did not mean this in a narrower, 'occult' sense of visions that were perceptible only by the initiate, but he was referring rather to our innate potential to develop our tangible vision, our sense of morphology, our organs of perception, and to practise and extend such capacities in both a sense-based and supersensible manner. Without doubt Rudolf Steiner was relying on farmers pursuing this path themselves. After describing the cosmic forces at work in the animal organism, he said: 'In this respect, those who are interested in these matters should develop their knowledge above all by learning to read the form. To be able to do this is of very great importance.[209]

Like all his courses for professional groups—doctors and teachers, scientists and priests—Steiner's lectures to the farmers aimed to prepare in his audience their own capacities for perception and knowledge, to give them a methodology they could draw on. Insight into the subtle life of nature should not and could not be the privilege of the spiritual researcher alone, but must in future become a possession of those working in agriculture. How 'we can look into the life and growth of all that goes on in and above the surface of the soil'[210] was the basic question for the survival and future of a sustainable agriculture. In a wonderful description of the forces constituting a tree and its close surroundings, its condensed astrality and (relative) etheric poverty, Rudolf Steiner said in lecture seven:

> In this realm it is easiest of all for one to attain a certain higher development. If you make the necessary effort, you can easily become esoteric in these domains. I do not say clairvoyant, but you can easily become clairsentient with respect to the sense of smell, especially if you acquire a certain sensitivity to the diverse aromas that proceed from plants growing upon the soil, and on the other hand from fruit tree plantations—even if only at the stage of blossoming—and from the woods and forests! Then you will feel the difference between a plant atmosphere poor in astrality, such as you can smell amongst herbaceous plants

growing close to the soil, and a plant world rich in astrality such as your nostrils detect when you sniff what is so beautifully wafted from the tree tops.

Accustom yourself to specialize your sense of smell—to distinguish, to individualize between the scent of more earthly plants and the scent of trees. Then, in the former case you will become clairsentient to a thinner astrality and in the latter to a denser astrality. You see, the farmer can easily become clairsentient. In recent times he has made less use of this faculty than in times of ancient, instinctive clairvoyance. The countryman can, as I said, become clairsentient with regard to smell.[211]

This 'higher form of experience' (Goethe) based on and prepared by his insights into nature, and the subsequent acquisition of a new kind of knowledge amongst farmers, was something Rudolf Steiner did not regard as an intellectual process. Instead the aim was to see these things 'quite clearly; then we shall gain a kind of sensitive cognition', a feeling perception.[212] Unlike many dehumanized, mechanical or schematized processes in industrial agriculture, Rudolf Steiner was concerned to foster a *'personal relationship'*[213] with substances, forces and beings, to nurture people's own, individual, intimate and insightful way of relating to things, which would itself have a schooling character. At one point in his Koberwitz lectures—in relation to composting questions—he said: 'Our specific measures must still depend on our inner feeling to a large extent. This inner feeling will develop rightly once we perceive the whole nature of the process.'[214] At the beginning of the twentieth century, the traditional 'sense', the ancient 'instinct' of farmers was scarcely present any longer. The new basis for understanding nature and agriculture facilitated by anthroposophy, however, aimed to lead to new capacities of feeling, to a 'personal relationship' as the starting point for individual processes of evaluation and decision-making. The specific themes which Rudolf Steiner embarked on and developed at Koberwitz were carefully considered and of fundamental significance. But drawing on these as examples he repeatedly tried to show how a new methodology of agriculture could be developed further. He gave no explicit answers to most of the questions he had been sent in advance by the Breslau group—and although such questions were useful, they were not posed again in the discussions. Much seems to indicate that Rudolf Steiner was hoping the farmers themselves might answer them, insofar as the course would enable them to pursue their work with greater insight, knowledge and practical application. The course was intended as an aid to self-education, albeit at the highest possible level.

*

Rudolf Steiner's emphasis on 'enlarging our observation of the life of plants and animals, but also the life of the earth itself, enlarging it greatly to encompass the cosmic aspect' was the thread running through the content of his Koberwitz lectures. The path he took to consider 'what conditions are necessary in order for the various branches of agriculture to thrive'[215] led his audience from observations of the living earth to the constituting substances and configuring forces of plants and animals; to the essence of an agricultural entity, its 'individuality' and its subtle interior space with all attendant mutual relationships, the 'intimate interplay' of nature, existing in specific and detailed ways between the soil, the plant realm and animals. In the penultimate lecture of the course Steiner spoke of these interactions in a striking, vivid way. All his descriptions led his audience to the bases for and possibilities of human intervention, to an agriculture of *deeds*, whereby they might nurture and order their farms by actively manuring the soil and plants, by applying preventive and healing interventions in relation to diseases, by 'regulating' the elements of nature, and finally also by feeding animals in an appropriate, animal-friendly way:

> The *principles* given in the course—showing how plants develop under various conditions, how animals develop, the principles of manuring and of combating weeds and pests as well as parasites and plant diseases—are all very pressing issues in agriculture today. After discussing these principles, we went on to talk about what actually needs to be done in order to *reform* the methods of manuring and the methods of combating weeds, pests, parasites and plant diseases.[216]

Back in Dornach Rudolf Steiner said that in Koberwitz he had pursued a path from presentation of 'principles' to possibilities for 'reforming' agricultural practice: from the spiritual origins of things to changing their current, overwhelmingly distorted form.

Steiner's description of the living soil and the plant realm, of the true nature and action of substances ('our chemists speak only of the corpses of the substances—not of the real substances, which we must rather learn to know as sentient and living entities...'[217]), his description of cosmic, planetary forces and agencies, of seasonal circumstances and constellations (working right down into the deep layers of the earth), were brilliant and at times breathtaking—but they were never an end in themselves. All the aspects Rudolf Steiner outlined aimed, rather, to illumine the natural foundations for appropriate human *action*. Immanuel Voegele had written to Steiner on 24 January to state his view that 'the farmer's task and work involves creating conditions for the secret forces of nature active in mineral, plant and animal kingdoms which will enable these forces to work and unfold in ways which they otherwise cannot.' Indeed, according to Rudolf Steiner at Koberwitz, it is the farmer's task to ensure that natural processes can unfold properly, to learn 'to see into the workings of nature ... then you will really take the processes of growth in hand'[218]—and to do so in a way which is determined by the needs of agriculture. In great detail he described the conditions necessary for the life and growth of plants in the interplay between earth and cosmos—so that, as he said, it would be possible to 'place oneself' into this context of forces with new understanding, and even, indeed—to a certain extent at least—to 'direct' growth through insight into the forces involved: 'The living forces are far more important for the plant than the mere substance forces or substances.'[219] This insightful and knowledgeable handling of active forces is what Rudolf Steiner called 'science': 'To experiment at random on these matters, as is done today, is no real science. The mere jotting down of isolated notes and facts—that's not science. Real science only arises when you begin to control the active forces.'[220]

The great majority of practical suggestions which Rudolf Steiner made were based on this dimension of human actions or interventions in relation to cosmic and earthly forces. Steiner's rationale for the different manure preparations to enliven the soil, as well as the approach he proposed for tackling plant diseases and pests of the most varied kinds, along with many other practical suggestions for agriculture, not only counted on existing forces and entities of both earthly and cosmic origin, but also configured their potential effect in specific ways in each instance—to promote or inhibit, redirect or transform. Already in his first lecture, Rudolf

Steiner described not only the cosmic forces of form but said at the same time:

> For we must ask ourselves: If forces come into the earth from moon, Venus and Mercury and affect the life of plants, by what means can the process be more or less quickened or restrained? By what means can the influences of moon or Saturn on the life of plants be hindered, and by what means assisted?[221]

According to Steiner, every kind of agriculture, even ordinary gardening, works in this way (rather than with merely material substances), starting from watering—which facilitates the action of (cosmic) forces of life and growth. At the same time the degree of differentiation Steiner opened up, and the scope of practical possibilities in relation to existing configurations of forces, was more than astonishing, and testified to his profound authority and knowledge. '*Real science only arises when you begin to control the active forces.*'

Rudolf Steiner's descriptions of new ways of combating pests, by drawing on cosmic forces and constellations did, however, considerably worry one member of his audience; the latter asked about potential misuse of the procedures recommended by Steiner: 'Some limit ought surely to be set, to prevent human beings from spreading destruction over the world.'[222] In his reply, Steiner engaged at some length with the question of responsibility thus raised, referring at the same time to the current need for such action ('For our needs today, we really have no choice to stop and discuss whether or not such things are permissible'[223]). He also spoke, though, about developments in human history and future requirements in relation to new knowledge and capacities.

[. . .] we should rather consider how to establish a kind of safety valve against misuse. It goes without saying that when these things are generally known and applied, abuses will be possible; that is quite evident. Nevertheless, it may be pointed out that there have been epochs of civilization on the earth when such things were known and applied in the widest sense. Yet it was possible for those among mankind who were in earnest, to keep these things within such bounds that the misuse did not occur.

Abuses did indeed occur in an epoch when far graver abuses were still possible, because these forces were universally prevalent. I mean during certain later periods of Atlantean evolution, when a far greater misuse occurred, leading to grave catastrophes.[224]

Many weeks later, in his 'Curative Education Course', Steiner returned to the problem of responsibility and the question raised at Koberwitz:

During the agriculture course at Koberwitz in Breslau, I suggested some guidelines for managing agriculture in the right way. Now an older farmer was present, who is also a member of the Anthroposophical Society. Throughout the course he could not get over a certain feeling, to which he repeatedly gave voice in discussions. He kept on saying: Yes, if you do this, you're using occult means to accomplish practical actions. Does this not have profound consequences for human morality? Could this not be misused, and thus be immoral? He could not get over this scruple, sensing something like black magic if these things were used, as they should and must be. So on one occasion I said very clearly: Yes, morality is required in all such things. This is why I assumed that all who took part in this course did so with the entirely moral stance of helping humanity and agriculture. This is why one should also regard the Agricultural Circle as a moral body which takes upon itself the task of applying these things in the right way. Magic, the gods, invoke them, but the difference between white and black magic consists only in the fact that white magic intervenes in a moral way, selflessly, whereas black magic does so in an immoral, selfish way. There is no other difference. [...] The most important thing here is to strengthen one's sense of responsibility.[225]

In his eight agricultural lectures, Rudolf Steiner spoke in a living, inspiring way out of the interior world, the inner existence of the realms of nature. His characterizations of, for instance, the tree, the birds, fertilizer preparations, the configurations of forces in yarrow and camomile, in nettle, oak bark and dandelion, profoundly impressed his audience by their power of insight founded in and made substantial by love. Steiner's descriptions had the quality of *being*—the nature of what he presented became vivid experience, acquired an almost tangible presence in the lecture room as he spoke. Many years prior to the Whitsun course at Koberwitz, he once spoke in Hamburg of Christian initiation and the sway of the 'holy spirit' in a highly purified soul body that was open to absorb the 'cosmic world I':

He who is thus illumined, who in other words has taken into himself the 'holy spirit' as Christian esotericism understands it, speaks from then on [...] in a different sense. How does he speak? He speaks in such a way that it is not his view when he speaks of Saturn, sun or moon, or about the various bodies constituting the human being, or the processes at work in world evolution. His views and opinions have nothing at all to do with what he says. When such a person speaks about Saturn, Saturn speaks from him. When he speaks about the sun, the spiritual being of the sun speaks through him. He is the instrument. His I has sunk from sight or in other words has become impersonal at such moments, and the cosmic world I now uses him as its instrument to speak through him.[226]

At Koberwitz, without doubt, Rudolf Steiner was speaking out of this dimension. Rudolf von Koschützki noted: 'Repeatedly, every day anew, I had the impression that inspirations flowed into him as he spoke.'[227] At the same time Rudolf Steiner was and remained in direct contact with his audience, in a form of inner dialogue with them. Outside of the discussion sessions, too, Rudolf Steiner perceived the concerns and questions of his listeners, and his lectures responded to them in a directly social and living way.

Despite this, some passages in the Koberwitz lectures were not easy to understand, and went way beyond the listeners' previous scope of experience and thinking. According to Koschützki much 'sounded [. . .] in our ears like a fairytale, so that we continually had to remind ourselves that *everything* we had so far heard from Rudolf Steiner had proven to be true.'[228]

*

At various points in the course, Rudolf Steiner entered more deeply into the importance of the farmer's inner stance. Asked whether stirring the preparations could not be done by machine, he said:

There can be no doubt, stirring by hand has quite another significance from mechanical stirring. A mechanically-minded person will not, of course, admit this. But you really should consider what a great difference it makes whether you really stir with your hand or by merely mechanical means. When you stir manually, all the delicate movements of your hand will come into the stirring. Even the feelings you have may then come into it.

Of course, people today will not believe that it makes any difference; but you can tell the difference even in medical matters. Believe me, it is not a matter of indifference whether a medicine is prepared in a more manual way or by more mechanical means. When a person works on substances himself, he gives them something which they retain [. . .] You must not smile at such things.[229]

In the differentiated characterizations of substance in his third lecture—after describing the 'astral spirituality' of nitrogen and its special significance in the tissue of nature and human existence—Rudolf Steiner spoke about the archetypal phenomenon of meditation which, at Koberwitz for the first time, he showed to be an enhanced sensitivity to the 'revelations' of nitrogen: 'By and by you grow into a conscious, living experience of the nitrogen all around you. Such is the real process in meditation.'[230] Prior to this Rudolf Steiner had described nitrogen substance not just as something that leads life into form, but as

The bearer of that mysterious sensitiveness which is poured out over the life of the earth.

It is the nitrogen which senses whether there is the proper quantity of water in a given district of the earth. If so, it has a sympathetic feeling. If there is too little water, it has a feeling of antipathy. It has a sympathetic feeling if the right plants are there for the given soil and so forth. In a word, nitrogen pours out over all things a kind of sensitive life [. . .] Nitrogen is not unconscious of what comes from the stars and works on through the life of plants, the life of earth. Nitrogen is the sensitive mediator, just as, in our nerve-sense system, it mediates our sensation. Nitrogen is, truly, the bearer of sensation.[231]

Then he continued, in reference to the farmer's spiritual stance and conduct:

If we have made ourselves receptive to nitrogen's revelations, we will begin to work as farmers in a very different way from before. We suddenly begin to *know* all kinds of things—they emerge. We suddenly begin to know all kinds of secrets that prevail in farm and farmyard [. . .] A learned man may say that the peasant is stupid. But in reality it is not true, for the simple reason that the peasant farmer— forgive me but it is so—is himself a meditator. What he meditates upon in the long winter nights is of very great value. He does indeed acquire a kind of method of spiritual perception, only he cannot express it. It suddenly rises up in him. We walk through the fields and suddenly the knowledge is there in us. We know something. Afterwards we put it to the test and find it confirmed. In my youth, at least, when I lived among peasant folk, I witnessed this again and again. It really is so. And from such things as these we must take our start once more. The merely intellectual life is not sufficient—it can never lead into these depths. We must begin again from such things. After all, the weaving life of nature is very fine and delicate. We cannot sense it—it eludes the coarse mesh of our intellectual concepts.[232]

Much seems to indicate that in this account Rudolf Steiner was considering neither advanced esotericists in his audience nor the farmers of olden times, but was suggesting that every farmer could access special capacities for acquiring insight and knowledge: by living with the spiritual content of his surroundings and the real 'substances' of existence with which

he holds daily intercourse. This is something, potentially, that
the farmer can grasp hold of consciously, a capacity he can
enhance. In response to a question about this, Rudolf Steiner
said that real inner work was of great significance in relation
to plant growth. He also replied positively, though briefly,
with specific explanations and limitations, to Ernst Stegemann's question about whether it might in principle be possible to combat pests by purely inner, meditative means:

> A very ticklish question was raised, for example, by our
> friend Stegemann in the discussion in the Hall the other
> day: whether parasites could be combated by such means—
> by means of concentration and the like. There can be no
> question about it: you can, provided you do it in the right
> way. In particular you would need to choose the right
> season—from the middle of January to the middle of
> February—when the earth unfolds its greatest forces,
> forces most concentrated in the earth itself. One could
> establish a kind of festival time then, and practise certain
> concentration procedures, and it would certainly be pos-
> sible to achieve an effect.
>
> As I said, it is a ticklish question, but it can be answered
> positively along these lines. The only condition is that it
> must be done in harmony with nature as a whole. You
> should be well aware that it makes all the difference
> whether you undertake a concentration exercise in the
> midwinter period or at midsummer.[233]

On the other hand, however, it could clearly be perceived at
Koberwitz that such aspects were not at the core of Rudolf
Steiner's efforts. He wanted to help bring about a practical
reform of agriculture in a way that would be generally relevant at a difficult period. People such as Ernst Stegemann had
been pursuing particular inner paths for years, but Steiner did

not wish to make this the prerequisite for the whole endeavour. In the field of agriculture, as elsewhere, he was calling for a 'new thinking' which took account of the whole human being. He did not take dogmatic and absolute positions, but lived with and in the modern world, with love for it: 'Whoever holds to Michael nurtures love in relation to the outer world, thereby finding the relationship to his soul's inner world that leads him to join with Christ.'[234]

Responding to a question about whether machines should be used at all in agriculture, or whether a machine-free agriculture might be desirable, he replied:

That cannot really be answered purely in agricultural terms. In the current life of today it is hardly a practical or topical question to ask whether machines are permissible. You can hardly be a farmer nowadays without using machines. Needless to say, not all operations are so akin to the most intimate processes of nature as the stirring we were speaking about just now. Just as we did not want to approach this intimate process with machines, so we can see that nature herself ensures that you can't get very far with machines in relation to aspects of nature which machines have nothing to do with. A machine will not help in the seed-forming process for instance. Nature does this for herself.

Really I think the question is not very topical. How can you do without machines today? On the other hand, I'd say that as a farmer you don't need to be crazy about machines either. Someone who is machine-mad will undoubtedly do worse as a farmer, even if his new machine is an improvement, than if he goes on using his old machine until it is worn out. However, in the strict sense of the word, these are no longer purely agricultural questions.[235]

In response to a farmer who asked whether the number of horn manure preparations for a larger area should be determined by calculation tables, or more out of feeling, Steiner said:

> No, I should not advise it. In such a case I think we really must use common sense. This is my advice: begin by trying it out thoroughly according to your feeling. When you have done all you can to get the most favourable results in this way, then, to give due heed to the world as it is today, set to work and translate your results into figures. In this way you can draw up proper tables which others can subsequently use.
>
> If someone is inclined to do it based purely on feeling, by all means do so. But he should not, in his attitude to others, behave as though he did not value figures and tables. The whole thing should be translated into calculable figures and amounts, which is what is really required today. You need cows' horns to make the preparation, but there's no need to grow bulls' horns in advocating it! This is precisely what leads so easily to conflicts. As far as possible I would advise you to compromise here, and bear in mind the way the world at large sees these things.[236]

Thus the Koberwitz course combined the subtle contents of a new initiate knowledge with a positive capacity to engage with the world—a phenomenon characteristic of the ancient mystery sites and their initiates, which later underwent further deepening through the Christ event (and sacrifice). Rudolf Steiner quite clearly belonged to this spiritual stream: he stood with both feet on the ground as was apparent from all the answers to questions he gave at Koberwitz, and had enormous, practical insight, and open-hearted human generosity. '*You need cows' horns to make the preparation, but there's no need to grow bulls' horns in advocating it!*'

*

The audience at Koberwitz Mansion were not only impressed by Steiner's agricultural lectures but also inspired and encouraged to tackle the tasks that lay before them. In his lectures Steiner did indeed succeed in deriving '*the most radical help from knowledge which at first glance seems remote*'[237]—and the farmers gathered at Koberwitz were determined to attempt the new beginning outlined by Steiner, even if they should meet with the strongest resistance from others of their profession:

> I know perfectly well that all this may seem utterly mad. I only ask you to remember how many things have seemed utterly mad which have nonetheless been introduced a few years later. If you had read the Swiss newspapers at the time you would have seen the reactions when someone first suggested building mountain railways: they ridiculed him. Yet within a short while the mountain railways were there, and today no one remembers that the person who thought of them was considered a fool. Here, as in all things, it is simply a question of opposing prejudice.[238]

In accordance with the hope expressed by Immanuel Voegele and Erhard Bartsch in their first letter to Rudolf Steiner, the Koberwitz course offered 'general spiritual-scientific foundations and specific suggestions' for a new agriculture—and showed what Immanuel Voegele, in January 1924, had called the '*outline and direction of the path*'.

On the afternoon of 11 June, after Rudolf Steiner's third lecture, the farmers founded the 'Agricultural Research Circle of the Anthroposophical Society' with Steiner's agreement and support. As he stated in his final lecture at Koberwitz, the course had only been able to give 'certain guidelines', yet these could be 'the foundation for manifold trials which will extend no doubt over a long period of time'.[239] In his previous lectures Rudolf Steiner had repeatedly said that his suggestions could and should be tested and tried out in agricultural practice, and in field trials: '[...] I should be glad if my statements were tested, for if you subsequently test them you will certainly find them confirmed.'[240] Elsewhere he often emphasized that much still needed empirical elaboration. This basic relationship between spiritual-scientific research and its practical application had already been developed by Steiner in many of his medical lectures and courses, starting with the first doctors' course in Dornach in the spring of 1920. From the beginning of the medical work Steiner had made clear that spiritual-scientific research and instruction had to be applied in clinical practice—and that only by this means would many details become evident, in relation to pharmaceutical processing of medicines or the frequency and dose of administration. At Koberwitz, too, he urged the farmers not so much to provide a—secondary—scientific 'proof' of his spiritual-scientific insights as to implement them in practice:

And as there is still the prevailing view—I don't want to call it prejudice—that all things must be subsequently verified, well and good! Set to work and try to verify them. If you do the experiments properly, you will find these things confirmed. If I had a farm, however, I would not wait for verification. I would apply the method at once, for I am sure that it will work. For me, spiritual-scientific truths are true by and of themselves, and we do not need to have them confirmed by something else, by external methods.

Our scientists have all made the mistake of looking to

external methods to verify these truths. In the Anthroposophical Society, too, they have done so. They at least should have known better; should have known that the truth of something can be self-sustaining. However, to get anywhere nowadays we must always verify things externally. It is no doubt a necessary compromise. In principle though, this is not necessary. For how do we know things inwardly? Through the fact that they stand inherently, by their own quality [...].[241]

The 'Agricultural Research Circle of the Anthroposophical Society' was thus not merely set up in order to compromise with modern demands by offering 'verification' but first and foremost to drive forwards the specific elaboration of these principles through specific questions, in close contact with the School at Dornach. Implicit in Rudolf Steiner's plan of the School and the Sections was a centre of initiation, research and teaching at Dornach (via the spiritual collaboration of Rudolf Steiner with each respective Section leader) and a community of people willing to apply the schooling received in their area of work, in sustained connection and ongoing dialogue with the Section. In January 1924, at the end of the first course to the 'young doctors', Rudolf Steiner had commented: 'In this sense, my dear friends, let us remain united: united in such a way that you see the Goetheanum here at Dornach as your centre, and really adhere to this centre so that it can work through you in the world.'[242]

With the group of young doctors Rudolf Steiner and Ita Wegman organized a correspondence 'newsletter', which was to contain questions submitted and regular replies from Steiner and Wegman.[243] With the group of farmers, likewise—while he was still at Koberwitz—Rudolf Steiner made agreements for the future of their common work. As a first step he asked that the farmers participating in the 'Research Circle' should send details of their farms to Dornach:

> Through your practical work you will know far better than we in Dornach about the nature of your soil, the kind of woodland there is and how much, and so on; what has been grown on the farm in the last few years and what the yield has been. We must know all these things which, after all, every farmer must know for himself if he wants to run his farm with understanding.
>
> These are the first details we will need: what there is on your farm, and what your experiences have been.[244]

Once the farmers have provided these details, the Science Section will then work out guidelines for setting up further experiments so that the practical pointers given in the course and in the accompanying discussions can actually be tried out. Thus in future everyone will be able to say, 'We have tried it and it works', even though some of these things may still seem strange right now. To this end, the Farmers' Circle will work very closely with the Science Section, and also with Dr Vreede, because astronomical information will be needed too. Of course, the whole School of Spiritual Science, and the Medical Section in particular, will also be involved in a variety of ways.[245]

From Dornach, from the School of Spiritual Science, 'will arise what is intended. There we will find, out of the heart of anthroposophy itself, scientific research and methods of the greatest exactitude,' stressed Rudolf Steiner in relation to further collaboration.[246]

From the beginning, Carl von Keyserlingk had placed great value on ensuring that the details elaborated in the Agriculture Course were kept within the circle of farmers, as spiritual content that needed safeguarding and further developing. In his last lecture at Koberwitz, Rudolf Steiner returned to this theme and affirmed it:

> Full recognition is due to the tolerance which has been shown, which has allowed a number of interested persons, not actually farmers, to share in this course. They must now recall the well-known opera and fix a padlock to their mouths, and not fall into the general anthroposophical error of proclaiming it immediately from every rooftop. We have often been harmed in this way, when people who don't really have any proper impetus for speaking but only repeat what they have heard, pass things on. It has done us much harm. It makes a great difference, for example, whether a farmer speaks of these things, or one who stands remote from farming life. It makes a difference that can easily be recognized.
>
> What would result if our non-farmer friends now started spreading these things as an interesting new chapter in anthroposophical teachings? It would be the same as has occurred with many of our lecture cycles. Others—including farmers—would begin to hear of these things from this and that quarter. As to the farmers, well if they hear of these things from a fellow farmer, they will say, 'What a pity, the man's gone crazy!' Yes, they may say this the first and second time, but eventually, when a good result is obtained, they will not feel such an easy conscience about rejecting it outright.
>
> If, on the other hand, farmers hear of these things from people who have no real authority to speak of them, people who are merely interested, that will set the cat among the pigeons. If that were to happen the whole thing would be discredited and its influence undermined. Therefore it is

essential for those of our friends who have been allowed to take part based only on their general interest, and who are not in the Agricultural Circle, to exercise the necessary self-restraint. They must keep it to themselves and not go spreading it far and wide as people are so fond of doing with anthroposophical things.

This principle, as our dear friend Count Keyserlingk announced today, has been decided on by the Agricultural Circle, and I can only say that I approve it in the very fullest sense.[247]

As one of those 'friends who have been allowed to take part based only on their general interest', Wilhelm Rath wrote in summary of the eight lectures of the course:

This wonderful course became a deeply joyous experience: a very ancient mystery wisdom, from which all agriculture once arose, was here given again to humanity anew. Agriculture can now remember the heavens, without whose blessings nothing on earth can thrive.[248]

Mercur fährt in das
geistige hinüber =
vorb. Stadium :

Venus = die Vereinigung
Gebärd für die große Welt.

Sonne - Exusiai = Offenbarer
Dynamis = die Kraftgeber
Kyriotetes = die

Mars } sie werden gewiss
Jupit } ... – Hauptes,
Saturn } bildend.

Rudolf Steiner: notebook entry relating to the different planetary
spheres and the passage through them of the human soul
(Ita Wegman Archive)

5

The Human Being's Cosmic Destiny

Rudolf Steiner's karma lectures in Breslau

When Dr Steiner spoke about the compost heap and preparation
stirring, one was immediately transported to an elemental peasant
atmosphere, and could almost believe this was his real profession,
in which he felt entirely at home [...] And what a wide span and
scope of experience we experienced from the same mind when, in
the evenings in Breslau, we hearkened to his descriptions of the
passage of human souls through the planetary spheres, their
onward journey from earth life to earth life and the laws of
destiny governing these lives in harmony with the elevated spirits
of the hierarchies...
Rudolf Meyer[249]

From Saturday onwards, the day before Whitsun, participants at the agricultural lectures in Koberwitz, all the members of the Anthroposophical Society in Breslau (whose
numbers swelled to several hundred people soon after the
First World War, due to the tireless work of Moritz Bartsch)
and numerous anthroposophists who had travelled there
specially to attend, met every evening at 8 p.m. in the great
lecture hall of the Viktoria School in Breslau to hear Rudolf
Steiner's karma lectures. 'Members have gathered here from
far and wide, so that the visit was especially rich', wrote
Steiner to Ita Wegman after his first evening lecture.[250] In his
letter to Arlesheim he did not mention that the many hun-
dreds of people stood to welcome him in the hall, at Moritz
Bartsch's initiative:

I discussed with the members the idea of standing up from our seats when the teacher entered the hall, just as my own pupils stand when I enter the classroom. As I was leading Rudolf Steiner from an adjoining room into the hall, the whole assembly stood up. Rudolf Steiner thanked them with both hands. But this truly great yet endlessly modest man found such an honour awkward. He said to me: 'They should stay sitting!'

As he mounted the podium, I sat down on his seat next to Frau Dr Steiner and quickly said to her: 'Herr Doktor wants the members to stay sitting, but I find it perfectly in order for them to stand.' 'So do I', she replied swiftly; and so they continued to stand each time.[251]

*

The systematically structured karma lectures which Rudolf Steiner gave from 16 February 1924 focused on the theme of the human I in its 'suffering and forming of karma' in relation to growing human self-knowledge. In the last week of May, shortly before his departure for the east, he had started to characterize, in particular, the cosmic aspects of destiny formation in the period between death and a new birth. In Breslau too, in direct relation to his agricultural lectures and their engagement with the theme of microcosm and macrocosm, Rudolf Steiner said by way of introduction:

Anthroposophical wisdom takes hold of human life in the profoundest way by highlighting the most comprehensive cosmic events, the mysteries of the whole world which, after all, are also microcosmically united again in the human being. But in everything that can dawn on us in this way out of the cosmos, that can become light-filled, lives something that shines not only into human days but into each hour of our lives as well; which, by engaging with life in all that relates to our destiny or karma, shines into what is intimately close to human hearts and what, as I say, touches on each hour of our existence. And so, starting from the most varied perspectives, I would like to speak to you during these days particularly about the anthroposophical foundations underpinning the ideas, the spiritual pictures, which can bring human karma close to us.[252]

Already in his first Breslau lecture, in close correspondence with his formulations at Koberwitz, Rudolf Steiner described the comprehending of 'spiritual lawfulness in the universe' as 'the task of anthroposophy today'.[253]

'How karma gradually forms', Rudolf Steiner states here, can only be understood by taking account of, and clearly perceiving, the after-death and pre-birth path of the human soul in the cosmos. In Breslau, Steiner primarily wished to describe 'how karma is gradually implanted as disposition in different heavenly spheres'.[254] He represented these 'spheres' (in development of his lectures in Paris) as the planetary stages of the cosmos or solar system, through which the human soul passes after death and before a new birth. At Koberwitz, the planets played a key role from the first agricultural lecture onwards, and Steiner highlighted the fact that an intimate relationship with worlds of cosmic forces and beings would be vital for an agriculture of the future. Already before he left for Silesia, Rudolf Steiner had decisively and strikingly embarked on the theme of the 'stars' in his last joinery workshop lecture in Dornach, in relation to the festival of Whitsun ('The Whitsun Thought as Feeling Foundation for Understanding Karma'). Rudolf Steiner returned to this on the evening of Whit Sunday, emphasizing in his second karma lecture at the Viktoria School that the 'passage' through the planetary spheres in the journey of life after death can lead to insight into the nature of the stars: 'And that, precisely, is the remarkable thing: that as we pass through these spheres we can perceive what the physical stars actually are.'[255] Speaking about the true being of the stars, Steiner went on to say:

> The gods as it were stroke the world in love. It's an entirely appropriate comparison: they caress the world, touching it at certain places. But their touching lasts a very long time, because the gods are enduring. This expression of love in the ether constitutes the stars. This is what they really are: there's nothing physical there. And seeing a star means sensing the same, in cosmic terms, as a touch or caress which a human being gives another. This is how we sense the love of divine spiritual beings as we look up to the stars. We have to realize that the stars are only signs of the presence of the gods in the universe. Our physical science will have much to learn if it wishes to move on from illusion to reality. But people will never come to self-knowledge, will never come to know their own being until they have entirely transformed this physical science—in relation to the non-terrestrial universe—into a spiritual science. Physical science only makes sense for the realm of earth, for only on earth does physical substance exist.[256]

Real human self-knowledge and thus experience of the self as an I that 'suffers and forms karma' requires a new cosmology, a new knowledge of the stars as part not only of a macro-cosmic and ecological knowledge (one needed throughout civilization) but also of real insight into destiny. Starting with his first Breslau lecture on 7 June, Rudolf Steiner intimately described the human soul's passage through cosmic and planetary spheres after death—the encounter with and real 'growing into' specific, hierarchically ordered beings or 'gods'. The 'stars are only signs', as he says, ' of the presence of the gods in the universe'. They enable the human being to lay aside his last earthly life with its physical and moral defects, transforming these into the impetus and power to redress and compensate for them:

> We may say therefore that if we gaze up to our planetary system with the sun—and we can gaze up in the same way to the other stars, for the rest of the starry dome is certainly also connected with the human being, as we will discuss—then, among other things, we can perceive human karma as it forms out of the cosmos. This moon, this Venus and Jupiter, are really not just what physical astronomy tells us they are. In their constellations, their mutual interplay, their shimmering and their whole existence, we must see them as the builders of human destiny, the clock from whose face we can read our destiny. In the constellations this clock shines down from the heavens. People once knew this in their ancient, instinctive mystery wisdom, but this ancient astrology, which is pure spiritual science, and which worked perceptively with the spiritual depths of existence, has come down to us in a shallow, dilettantish form. And only through anthroposophy will something arise again which allows us to perceive in a truly spiritual context how the great clock of destiny governs human life here on earth according to its laws.[257]

According to Rudolf Steiner, knowledge of the human being and destiny cannot be divided from knowledge of the cosmos or from a real knowledge of the stars, for we bear within us the planets' formative forces and their spirituality, in both a physically corporeal and moral sense. Every approach to understanding a human destiny is thus also an approach to the cosmos, to its configuration of forces and formative world: 'If one learns to understand a human destiny, one learns at the same time to understand secrets of the whole star system. In looking upon a human destiny one gazes upon the mysteries of the cosmos.'[258] Besides pondering thoroughly on these connections, Rudolf Steiner said in Breslau, we should *experience* them profoundly:

> Karma as the configuration of destiny in a human life is so vast, so elevated, so majestic for he who gains insight into it that, simply by virtue of understanding how karma is related to the universe, to the spiritual cosmos, he grows into a quite different mode of sensing and feeling—not merely theoretical knowledge. And everything one acquires through anthroposophy should, after all, not be just the appropriation of theoretical knowledge but should always gradually work upon the way we think and feel, leading us ever deeper with our heart from the worms in the soil to a felt experience of the world of spirit.[259]

*

In Breslau, Rudolf Steiner characterized in detail the gradual process whereby moral deficiencies of an individual life on earth are retrospectively experienced, evaluated and laid aside in the after-death moon sphere, followed by the overcoming or dispelling of dispositions to and consequences of illness in the Mercury sphere, which he engaged with very fully:

> As he enters the Mercury sphere, the human being is further cleansed and purified. Once he has laid aside what is, one can say, morally unusable for the cosmos in the moon sphere, the human being still retains the spiritual pictures that reflect his physical inabilities or weaknesses. He retains in himself the dispositions to and results of illness which he

underwent here on earth. Now this will surprise you, but it is true to say that in the life between death and a new birth we first lay aside our moral deficiencies and only later the physical ones—that is, when we reach the Mercury sphere. Here the human being's soul is cleansed and purified from all he experienced during life on earth: the various processes of illness. In other words, we are made entirely whole and healthy in the Mercury sphere [...] When someone is ill, the soul also undergoes an experience of illness; so does the spirit. And once the human being has laid aside the physical body at death, he initially still retains the effects of those experiences he underwent through processes of illness. But in the Mercury sphere these are entirely laid aside with the aid of those beings we call archangeloi.[260]

When Rudolf Steiner spoke these words about the '*Mysteries of the Mercury Sphere*' on Whit Sunday evening, his Koberwitz comments on processes of illness in agriculture, and means of healing them, had not yet been uttered. In Breslau he was speaking exclusively about the human being, whereas in Koberwitz he spoke about the living soil, and about plants and animals. The element of healing, however, permeated both (and also the many patient consultations at Koberwitz). Picking up on the esoteric Class lesson he had given in the morning, he spoke as follows on Whit Sunday evening about the Mercury mysteries and their connection with medicine:

These wise initiates of the ancient mysteries knew that only the supersensible beings of Mercury could give insight into the processes of healing. For this reason the Mercury mysteries were formed in such a way that, in response to the corresponding rite, beings dwelling on Mercury could indeed descend to the altar dedicated to Mercury worship, and the priests of the Mercury mysteries could hold converse with these spiritual beings who thus descended. The medicine of those times was certainly something received in the Mercury mysteries in this way. The beings—who were not even necessarily always the same ones, though they were felt to be—who descended to the altars, were given the name of the god Mercury. People received the ancient mystery medicine in acknowledgement that this was communicated by the god Mercury to his priest physicians. And this is how healing was accomplished.

Today, too, spiritual science relies on the right preparation by initiates so that the beings of our cosmos can descend to earth. Initiates in today's mystery wisdom know very well that it is of essential importance to enter into dialogue with the beings of the cosmos.[261]

Then, continuing his observations on the planets, Rudolf Steiner described how the love power of the Venus sphere accompanies the disabled and 'mutilated' human being—after laying aside his moral and physical deficiencies—into sun existence, where the chief work on human karma occurs in the realm of the second hierarchy. This is the longest after-death or pre-birth period of development, when the physical disposition and 'thorough organization' of the future body occurs, along with elaboration of a person's moral biography. In the later passage through the planetary spheres of Mars, Jupiter and Saturn, Rudolf Steiner says that particular potential capacities are acquired for forming the forthcoming biography as we engage with the high hierarchical beings of these realms.

As he continued with his evening lectures at Breslau, Rudolf Steiner passed on to characterizing these planetary influences on the forming of human biographies and personalities by citing well-known individuals who had played a role in world history. The 'Saturn' characterization of Friedrich Schiller on 10 June was one highpoint of these examples. Speaking of the inner mood needed to fully attend to such descriptions, he said:

> In order to gaze upon the karma of an individual human being, and indeed upon one's own, today too we really need the right mood, the right attitude of soul. In fact every karmic observation becomes a profanity if one receives it in the kind of mood that inevitably proceeds from modern education, civilization, from the schooling of our times. Examinations of karma should really only enter the soul in a sacred mood, one that is completely imbued with reverence. Each time that we approach a karmic truth we should really have a sense that we are as it were lifting the veil of Isis.[262]

Rudolf Steiner spoke of the need to acquire a 'sacred mood' for approaching observations on human destiny—and repeatedly pointed out that the study of historical individuals was merely a methodological step towards future self-knowledge, as the true goal of inner schooling.

In his nine evening lectures in Breslau, Rudolf Steiner opened up other, still more far-reaching perspectives on human destiny and knowledge of destiny. He spoke extensively about his own research method, about the return of groups of people connected by destiny with one another in historical evolution, about ways to recall one's own previous incarnations during sleep—and about the process of morning awakening against the background of the 'I that suffers and forms karma'. Once again linking with the Koberwitz lectures and ancient 'peasant culture', he said:

> Simple people who once lived a rustic life in the country—a way of life that is increasingly rare—knew of such things,

and that is why they did not wish to be shaken quickly awake; this is because when one is roused suddenly, and enters waking life without a gradual transition, one is torn out of this kind of intimate experience. That's why the farmer or peasant used to say one should never look at the window straight away when one wakes, but instead look away from it, staying with the darkness for a while to observe what arises from one's sleep. The peasant doesn't like looking at the window straight away, nor to be woken with a sudden shock. Instead he prefers to awaken gently or naturally, with a church bell that rouses him every day at the same time, so that he can prepare himself for this moment throughout the night as he sleeps. Then things slowly dawn, the church bell slowly resonates into life, and then, in the morning, he can sense his destiny: the events and circumstances of destiny, rather than the free occurrences of the will. That's what he likes, and will detest being woken by an alarm clock, even if 'civilized' people prefer it; for it is certain that this will drive one out of all spiritual experience, naturally much more so than the window one happens to glance at as one awakens. But our modern culture has allied itself with materialism in everyday life, and continues to do so. There is much in modern life which makes it impossible for people to perceive or observe the spirit living and weaving in the world. The more someone observes that indefinite or almost half-mystical quality that can shimmer into his life from sleep, the more he can begin to notice his karma.[263]

Rudolf Steiner's evening lectures in Breslau culminated in the realm of forces—permeated by the first hierarchy—of the metabolic and limb system, in the will aspect of human existence from which future karma is born.

*

For those who heard them, the nine Breslau karma lectures became unforgettable. They implicitly invoked the individual, his individual biography, task in life and future potential, his capacity for community and his membership of a group, yet they left listeners free—and Rudolf Steiner only asked that the connections he described should be weighed and pondered inwardly, with 'soul, feeling and love':[*]

> One must regard such things not only with dry reason but with soul, feeling and love; but in such a way that these become as clear and bright as only reason usually is, really developing perception and knowledge. Reason can only elaborate images of outer nature. If you believe you will come to anything other than an outward picture of nature by this means you are wrong. This other aspect is one you can only attain when soul, feeling and love become powers of perception and knowledge. When one transposes oneself back in karmic development in the way suggested, only then will one gradually be able to work one's way through to a vision of how karma works. But then the whole soul must participate. This is why what lies in such descriptions of karma must take hold of the whole human being.

The farmers with an anthroposophical orientation (or interest) who had come to Koberwitz to deepen their work and place their will at the service of a really new beginning, a 'forthcoming karma', absorbed Steiner's characterizations of destiny into their souls in a profound way. Rudolf Meyer later wrote that in Koberwitz and Breslau Rudolf Steiner

---

[*] Translator's note: the word translated here as 'soul' is the almost untranslatable 'Gemüt', which means both heart and mind, or inner disposition of soul.

'*knew how to unite loving devotion to earthly tasks with courage towards the stars*'.[264] Meyer's formulation also really applied to the agricultural lectures themselves, whose mighty macrocosmic aspects had to be absorbed 'courageously'. But in the evening lectures in Breslau, Rudolf Steiner combined these descriptions with the idea of destiny, with the human soul's cosmic home: the 'location' working on into biographical resolves of great and significant scope, which could also be a group resolve of people incarnated together. Whether the farmers themselves had asked Rudolf Steiner questions relating to destiny is not known. Johanna von Keyserlingk only mentioned that an artist asked him about previous incarnations of Caspar Hauser before one of the Breslau lectures:

> The following day Rudolf Steiner brought him the answer: he had done spiritual research both where Caspar Hauser had entered physical existence and also where he had been murdered, but he could not find any indication of a former or a subsequent incarnation. He was a higher being who had a quite special task on earth.[265]

Rudolf Steiner was very pleased at how the karma lectures were received in Breslau, as he emphasized on his return to Dornach. People's hearts were absorbing and taking up the inwardly esoteric 'character' with which the Christmas Foundation Meeting had begun. Rudolf Steiner also gave two esoteric Class lessons in Breslau on 12 and 13 June: 'I showed how the path to spirit knowledge, and soul experiences in the transition from sensory to spiritual perception, can be understood through inner soul work.'[266]

Christus in der Sonne — der
Führer aller Menschen der Erde —
Der die Bewußtseinsseelen führt
dazu, die Trennungen der Erzengel
vorzubereiten für die Sammlung
durch Michael = die Sonne soll
so in den Blickpunkt des
Menschen gestellt sein, dass
das Kopernikusschema nur als
Orientierung dient : das muß
herauskommen. =

Rudolf Steiner: notebook entry relating to the mission of Christ and the Michael school (Ita Wegman Archive)

6

The Human Being, the Era of Michael and Nature

Rudolf Steiner's addresses to young people

I saw open hearts and engaged souls before me as I spoke. We
talked about the nature of the youth movement and the goals which
our time requires of it.
Rudolf Steiner[267]

Many young people who felt—often freely and informally—
that they belonged with anthroposophy, who had survived
the First World War and came from the wider youth movement and the 'Wandervogel' movement, feeling connected
with nature, were waiting for Rudolf Steiner in Breslau. This
included the group of young farmers around Immanuel
Voegele and Erhard Bartsch, who had prepared the Koberwitz course.

On 24 February, in the newsletter of *Das Goetheanum*
magazine, Rudolf Steiner suggested the possibility of developing a future Youth Section, and urged young anthroposophists to engage in dialogue about this. According to
Steiner he had assumed leadership of the General Anthroposophical Society also in order to encourage young people
and future generations to enter this society and engage with
its cultural tasks: 'To publicly represent anthroposophy does,
surely, require a quite different style. And this was also one of
the factors which persuaded me to assume leadership.'[268] In
four further articles published in March, Rudolf Steiner

wrote about the 'youth question'—about the longing of modern youth for a world view rather than 'a science without the larger picture'; about their suffering at the 'chilliness of a civilization devoid of a world view' and about his own youth during the last third of the nineteenth century as the 'Kali Yuga' or dark age was ending and 'digging the grave of the spirit in human experience of matter'. Already in these articles in March, Rudolf Steiner was emphasizing the real wind of change blowing through civilization, despite all retardant forces and current problems and difficulties: 'The age of light has dawned however. As yet this is not felt since most people still bear the after-effect of the old darkness in their souls. But he who has a sense for spiritual beings, can know that it has grown "light".'[269] Spiritual science, as Steiner wrote on 23 March, could help souls 'who wish to awaken': 'It does not wish merely to give people knowledge, but to bring life close to them. Then it will be within their freedom to transform knowledge into life.'[270] On 30 March, twelve months before he died, he published the following sentences—among others—in the Dornach newsletter: 'If young people [...] reflect on their true experiences, they will find that these are like questions to them, and that the esoteric approach of the Anthroposophical Society brings them attempts, at least, at some answers.'[271]

*

The first gathering with young people who had asked to meet Rudolf Steiner took place on the afternoon of Whit Monday, in a rented concert hall in Tauentzienstrasse in the centre of Breslau, also used for sacraments and services of the Christian Community. The 23-year-old priest and leader of youth work in Breslau, Kurt von Wistinghausen, greeted Steiner and thanked him for coming to speak with them. By way of introduction, Wistinghausen said Rudolf Steiner had 'world tasks' to fulfil, and thus his appearance in such a 'very modest, randomly assembled group of young people'[272] was something very special: 'We are not just academics but also merchants and officials, and mostly not even members of the Anthroposophical Society.'[273]

Rudolf Steiner, who had brought executive council members Elisabeth Vreede, Guenther Wachsmuth and Marie Steiner with him to the meeting, along with a few older anthroposophists, spoke in his address of how the youth movement should be taken very seriously indeed, and that the anthroposophical and youth movements were connected by an '*inner destiny*'. Elaborating on this he said:

> If I draw on what I myself have experienced through many decades in the struggle to create a community of people who seek the spirit, and if I connect this with what has emerged as youth movement roughly since the turn of the century, I have to say that what very few felt 40 years ago— and which, since so few felt it, was scarcely noticed—is now felt within the youth movement as it grows and becomes ever more widespread.[274]

Then Rudolf Steiner described the difficulties young people face living in a world whose institutions—based on scientific materialism—have become alien to the human being, and also the general experience young people have of meeting 'masks' rather than real people. Young people today, he said, were not prepared to participate in and perpetuate this dehumanized and formalized 'culture'; their discarding of traditions and conventions was more than a generational conflict: a real turning point had arrived of a kind previously 'unknown to humanity, at least in historical times and also, largely, in prehistoric times [. . .] *A radical turning point in time has come.*'[275] The decisive nature of young people in the modern world, but also the difficulty of their lives, was connected, he said, with the 'depths of their souls'. Subconsciously the younger generation had undergone significant experiences at the end of the nineteenth century, during the time immediately before they incarnated. As in his March articles, in Breslau Rudolf Steiner placed emphasis on the radical new departure, the caesura in history, which occurred as the 'dark age' ended:

> People say that at the turn from the nineteenth to the twentieth century the so-called dark age came to an end, and that a new, light-filled age has started. This is quite certain: those who can gaze into the world of spirit know it is true. The fact that not a great deal of light is making its appearance does not contradict this. People have become habituated to the old darkness, and just as a ball continues rolling once it has received an impetus, so this dark age is rolling on for a while, rolls on through inertia.[276]

The 'onward-rolling' trend of civilization, said Steiner, still asks for 'scientific' confirmation, professional certification and formal proofs. Young people, however—like the anthroposophical movement—desired real, soul-spiritual experience in the place of external verification: '*What counts is that we come, in fact, to real experience.*'[277] The core of the anthroposophical movement on earth, Steiner continued, consisted of people who at the turn of the century had embarked on a path different to that of the rest of civilization. In June 1923, in his great Dornach lectures on the history of the anthroposophical movement, Rudolf Steiner had first spoken of the 'homeless souls' who had left the 'general march' of civilization and had become anthroposophists;[278]

now he returned to this theme, also in relation to the human being's cosmic dimension:

> [...] The anthroposophical movement unites people from every walk of life, from every profession and age group, who felt, at the turn of the century, that the human being must place himself into the whole universe in a quite different way. He must not only have something verified and proven, but must also be able to experience something.[279]

The spiritual dimension of experience in anthroposophy was something Rudolf Steiner had focused on ever more prominently since the Christmas Foundation Meeting. Anthroposophy itself should be intensively experienced and contemplated. In May 1924, shortly before his departure for Breslau and Koberwitz, Rudolf Steiner wrote in the newsletter to the members of the Anthroposophical Society: 'Esotericism rests on [...] an interiorizing activity in the communication of truths. This making inward should be seen as part of the impetus which the Christmas Foundation Meeting tried to bring into the Anthroposophical Society.'[280] Speaking to the 'young doctors' in January, after a differentiated characterization of anthropological and cosmological connections, he said:

> All such knowledge is only of value if it sinks directly into our moral being, if one can experience an inward shock at the fact that, through human activity, one descends by this means into a sense and feeling for the cosmos. And meditating, particularly for physicians, does not involve merely chewing over thoughts but bringing before the soul such connections, and entering into inwardly differentiated feelings which allow one to experience inner shocks of all possible kinds.[281]

Rudolf Steiner's Koberwitz course was doubtless imbued with this experiential dimension, albeit in a cautious way given the large, heterogeneous audience, who primarily expected practical aids and suggestions. But when speaking to the young people in Breslau, Rudolf Steiner directly addressed the necessary internalization involved in heart thinking, in accordance also with his statement of 30 March: 'If young people [. . .] reflect on their true experiences, they will find that these are like questions to them, and that the esoteric approach of the Anthroposophical Society brings them attempts, at least, at some answers.'

As he continued, Rudolf Steiner engaged ever more directly with the spiritual 'underground depths of soul' of the people before him, most of whom had been born in the latter years of the nineteenth century. He spoke of the Michael age starting from 1879, and indeed of the 'Michael movement' in the world of spirit, whose witnesses they were, he said, due to their prebirth experiences and intentions:

And if I now speak more of the underlying depths of existence, it is after all because I see that young people, who only recently descended to physical existence from the world of spirit, have done so with quite different demands on life from those who descended earlier. Why is this so? You don't have to believe me, but for me it is knowledge, not just belief. You see, before one descends into physical existence, one passes through all kinds of experience in the world of spirit which are more rich in content, more powerful than what one experiences on earth. This is not to underestimate the value of life on earth. Freedom could never evolve without earthly life. But the life between death and birth is more magnificent. *The souls who have descended are those that now indwell you, my dear friends.*

These souls really were granted sight of a hugely significant spiritual movement in super-earthly regions, unfolding behind physical existence. This is the movement which I call the Michael movement within our Anthroposophical Society. It is so. Whether today's materialistic person wishes to believe it or not, it is so! And, in the context of the spiritual leadership and guidance of the earth and humanity, the leading power for our times, for today—one might call it by a different name, but I call it the Michael power—is really striving for a reforming of all soul nature on earth. The people who grew so clever intellectually in the nineteenth century have no inkling of the fact that the world of spirit has relinquished the stance of soul which, in the nineteenth century, became the most enlightened out-look; that its end approaches and that a Michael commu-nity of beings who never descend to earth yet guide humanity, is striving to develop in humanity a new stance of soul. The death of the old civilization has finally arrived.[282]

This stance of soul of people today is to be replaced by another which will emerge from the human being himself, will be experienced in the human being's core. This is the striving of spiritual beings who, one can say, are recognized by the signs of the times, and have taken over leadership of our age. *The souls who have descended to earth in your bodies have seen this Michael movement and have descended bearing the impress of the Michael movement.* And here they have lived their way into a humanity that really excludes the human being, making him into a mask. And so the youth movement is really a wonderful memory of pre-earthly life, of the most important impressions of this pre-earthly life. And if one has these indefinite, subconscious memories of pre-earthly life, this sight of a striving for renewal of the human stance of soul, one finds nothing of it here on earth. This is what is really going on in young hearts and minds today.[283]

Then, in relation to the anthroposophical movement, Rudolf Steiner continued:

> The anthroposophical movement reveals itself and emerges from the Michael movement. Its task is to bring to human beings what is needed and desired. Here on earth the anthroposophical movement wishes to gaze up to the Michael movement. Young people bring with them a memory of pre-earthly life. This leads them together, as destiny. That is why all that has unfolded between the youth movement and the anthroposophical movement appears to be something really quite inward, not a matter of earthly circumstances only, but of spiritual circumstances inasmuch as these are intrinsic to the human being.[284]

The 'reforming of all soul nature on earth' or the introduction of a 'new stance of soul' to humanity was something, said Steiner, that lived in the underground depths of soul of young people in the first decades of the twentieth century. This dictated their life concerns and difficulties, but also their will to change the world. The younger generation was striving and seeking for the other, for community and real connection— but the human being and his essential nature could only be found in the spirit:

> Now it is the case that one cannot find the human being in other people if one does not know how to seek him in a spiritual way; for the human being is, after all, a spiritual being, and in encountering him only outwardly we cannot find him even though he is there.[285]

Here Rudolf Steiner briefly sketched out the false paths and dangers of a movement whose subliminal search, of both an existential and epoch-making kind, could be restricted to social and soul togetherness *and* could enable other powers and forces to misuse the longings at work in it. In 1914 the 'Wandervogel' generation had set off for the First World War with great enthusiasm, in the hope that the old orders would be dissolved—and more than half its members had lost their lives there. In 1924, in contrast, Adolf Hitler and the Nazi party were working systematically to harness the young generation to their purposes, making intentional use of all available forces. On 12 April an alert observer of the Hitler trial in Munich, the philosopher Ernst Bloch, wrote in his diary: 'One should not underestimate the extent to which young people are in Hitler's grip. [...] Hitler, Hitlerism and fascism are the ecstasies of middle-class youth.'[286]

*

In the context of his address to young people in Breslau on Whit Monday, Rudolf Steiner spoke of the power of egotism and psychological self-involvement as a problem to be overcome. Extreme subjectivity, he said, made it impossible to find a way to reach the other: 'Each person speaks and acts out of himself alone. Just think how different that is immediately if one can feel one's way into the other.'[287] Anthroposophy, on the other hand, he said, was a path of schooling that forms organs of perception and knowledge—to perceive and grasp life in the given world with its specific conditions of existence:

One has to find one's way into something objective. Egotism is the signature of our age. If we begin to find true interest in the human being, this egotism cannot continue. One thoroughly overcomes it by first overcoming it in something that is so hard for the soul to grasp as anthroposophy. There one has to relate to one's inner being and in doing so one strips away egotism and can then find one's way to the other. That emerges as fruit.[288]

As long ago as the end of the eighteenth century, Goethe stated that a person seeking knowledge must, with 'harnessed selfhood' and 'growing objectivity' succeed in taking the measure of knowledge, the evaluative data, not from himself but from the sphere of the things which he observes.'[289] Already in his youth Rudolf Steiner further elaborated and intensified this Goethean relationship to the world and knowledge, from an early stage emphasizing that the human being's natural environment and the study of nature could become the '*teacher of selflessness*'.[290] The anthroposophical path of schooling was based, he said, on 'insightful selflessness'. He often spoke of how this selflessness was not just an element of anthroposophical schooling and research but in certain respects also a precondition for (and result of) absorbing it fully: 'One thoroughly overcomes egotism by first overcoming it in something that is so hard for the soul to grasp as anthroposophy' he stressed on Whit Monday in Breslau. Three years previously, he stated in his first theology course in Dornach:

> You see, what someone acquires in anthroposophy, quite irrespective of how far he himself gets as researcher or how much insight he gains [...] requires him to give up a considerable amount of his I, I mean his egotism. A certain selflessness is part and parcel of this emergence from oneself, of entering fully into the world. You can say that one has to tear a great deal free from habitual egotism, quite radically, to find a truly human relationship to even the simplest anthroposophical insights. A sense of the world

must develop strongly to balance the sense of I, and gradually something grows as one pursues this seeming path of knowledge which not only resembles ardent love but is the equivalent of it; all this grows and develops. And basically one does indeed learn to know the meaning of devotion to objective reality as one studies anthroposophical content.[291]

At Koberwitz Rudolf Steiner spoke of the conditions sustaining agriculture, or rather—he spoke out of them. 'Devotion to objective reality' related to the being and existence of the other—and thus also to the cow horn and the manure, the compost and the animal, the soil and the nettle, the world and the inner world of the beings of nature.

*

After his introductory address, Rudolf Steiner engaged extensively with the young people's questions, their troubles and concerns relating to existing professions—which he emphatically said must be entirely 'reconfigured' in future to make a life of human dignity possible. At Koberwitz Rudolf Steiner was in the process of highlighting elements of such 'reconfiguration' and renewal, not just in agriculture but in the farmer's profession overall. This—unexpressed—dimension of the eight lectures had been living intrinsically in the young people's preparation group, as question and plea; and in January Immanuel Voegele had written to Steiner: 'As long as the possibility still exists of an agriculture course according to spiritual scientific principles, it seems to me that I ought not to cease trying. *This is because I believe that fulfilment of my hope will enable me to engage in my profession as a whole human being in a way that accords with the spirit and with reality.*'

The necessary renewal of human life and professions could only be accomplished in communities, stressed Rudolf Steiner in Breslau. To a young man who spoke of being 'pulverized' by the world of work, he replied: '[Today] one must find a [spiritual] path alongside one's profession, and find enough people for this path to ensure that a power arises to reshape the professions.'[292] Since his interlocutor also referred to Steiner's characterizations of Michael, the former returned to this theme, and went on to say:

Much can happen to ensure such a power develops, as I described when speaking of the power of Michael. Yet this must come to expression in great festivals of Michael. We should really come to the point where the germinating power of the future, small intimations of which we can sense, can arise in festivals of hope and expectancy. Particularly in festivals where people are brought together only through hope and expectancy rather than through sharply delineated ideals, they should have before them the picture of Michael with his directing gaze, his pointing hand and spiritual armour. Such a festival must come about. Why has it not yet arisen? As firmly as I will insist that this festival must emerge from the core of the anthroposophical movement, nevertheless I will equally firmly hold it back until the strength is there to celebrate it in a worthy way. The times are too grave to do this shallowly. When it is celebrated in a worthy way it will impart mighty impulses to humanity. This is why we must wait until the strength to do it exists. Not just a vague, pie-in-the sky, hazy uplift from the idea of Michael is needed, but an awareness that a new soul world must be founded amongst human beings. The Michael principle is indeed what leads and guides us. This involves an experience of community in which we can work towards a Michael festival period, when the spirit of future hope, the spirit of expectancy can hold sway.[293]

As on Good Friday in Dornach, so here too, on Whit Monday in Breslau, Rudolf Steiner thus emphasized the need for future 'Michael festivals' in a striking and compelling way:

> Above all I still remember the impression made on me when Dr Steiner placed the figure of the archangel Michael before us, as though he were standing there in the room at that moment. As he described the shimmering armour, the gesture and the gaze of the archangel, his own figure grew more upright and intense as though he himself wore this armour, and his own gaze looked far away and beyond us. (Kurt von Wistinghausen[294])

In another reminiscence of this event, von Wistinghausen wrote:

> While Rudolf Steiner was speaking of future 'festivals of hope and expectancy', his own figure straightened and grew intense before the very eyes of those present, his gaze looking away over our heads into the distance and assuming a steely shimmer, which appeared to us as a reflection of a world which he directly perceived. With raised voice he said that in these festivals one must have the picture before one 'of Michael with directing gaze, pointing hand and spiritual armour'. It was a moment of striking, destiny-forming power.[295]

*

At the end of the Whit Monday gathering, Rudolf Steiner was again asked about the young people in the 'Wander-vogel' movement. In his reply he spoke once more of the need for a true perception and knowledge of nature ('today people can wander through the whole world and see nothing')—and reiterated on the schooling of capacities. In this connection, referring to his book *Knowledge of the Higher Worlds*, he said:

> To see something one has to have a heart. But if one is prevented from being a whole human being, already in primary school, one does not see what is there in nature. If one can re-engage with all that is present in nature, then one will also discover something different in *Knowledge of the Higher Worlds* from what others find. This book, certainly, was not written to exclude nature but definitely with an eye to it. People have said that you can tell from my style of writing that I write on the typewriter since I have no time during the day. This criticism is certainly unfounded. I have never yet taken a typewriter to bed, where I write most of my pieces. That would seem grotesque. It all depends how things are conceived. They are absolutely conceived with an eye to nature. *Knowledge of the Higher Worlds* is definitely a 'Wandervogel' book. I see no contradiction; it's due to the fact that one is neither entirely one thing nor the other. Experiencing nature as a 'Wandervogel' will also enable you to experience this book, which really shouldn't be a book at all. It only looks as though it is one.[297]

Rudolf Meyer, who took part in the youth gathering, reported as follows on further statements Steiner made there:

> 'It is true however,' he went on to say, 'that after one has practised the exercises given in this book, one might reach the stage of stopping at the first wayside flower one comes across, for one can find the whole of the starry firmament hidden therein. Perhaps it is not necessary to "wander" so

far if one discovers how to penetrate the heights and depths of the cosmos by means of simple phenomena.'[298]

At the end of the gathering on 9 June, Rudolf Steiner said he was pleased that no transcript had been made of it: 'It was my intention never to have printed certain things one says only in personal conversation. I am so glad that no one is taking down what we said today.'[299] When Kurt von Wistinghausen then had to admit that Lili Kolisko had in fact recorded it in shorthand, Rudolf Steiner laughed 'very heartily'.[300] Nevertheless, the youth group decided that the next meeting with Rudolf Steiner, which took place two days later on 11 June at the Viktoria School, and consisted of questions and answers, should not be documented.

*

The meetings with Rudolf Steiner in Breslau meant a great deal to the 'random assembly' of young people for their further life and work, both within and outside the Anthroposophical Society. Never before had Rudolf Steiner spoken in this way—both distressing and encouraging—about the theme of Michael as inherent in the context of spiritual incarnation at the turn of the century. Rudolf Steiner pointed to possibilities and dangers in the present and future which it would be essential to consider in order to work in a manner both constructive of civilization and personally fruitful. We do not know to what extent the individuals present were able to directly absorb this message. But Steiner was very consciously addressing these themes in Breslau, in the context of the Koberwitz course and at the Whitsun period. Karin Ruths-Hoffmann, a participant, wrote about the meetings of young people with Steiner: 'The intensity of these hours, together with the karma lectures in the evenings, must have had a tremendous spiritual effect.'[301] This formulation seemed to refer beyond the circle of participants towards an objectively important event for everything to come.

The Breslau talks for young people were also of outstanding significance for those amongst Steiner's young audience who felt particularly devoted to agriculture and Koberwitz—not just in relation to the specialist knowledge they were absorbing from the 'private course' but also the common future task. On Whit Monday in Breslau, Rudolf Steiner said:

> [...] The more we relinquish the desire to achieve something speedily and immediately, the more we strive to work industriously to cultivate what initially should be a spiritual community working towards something, the better this will be. That is what we must take account of.

At the end of the Koberwitz lectures, the younger participants in the 'Agriculture Course' asked Rudolf Steiner whether he had another hour to spare for them. He gladly agreed—and the last meeting with him took place on the morning of his departure, on Tuesday 17 June, at Koberwitz.

To Herr Dr Rudolf Steiner
with whole-hearted thanks
for the spiritual wealth
given in Breslau and Koberwitz
at Whitsun 1924,
from the Breslau Anthroposophical Society

A message of thanks from the Breslau Anthroposophical Society
(Rudolf Steiner Archive)

7

'Now We Have Accomplished That Important Work As Well'

Rudolf Steiner's departure

But the course—what shall I say—that was a splendid affair. I would be able to recognize Herr Dr Steiner again among thousands! He said goodbye to each of us individually and thanked us for the pains we had taken. Yes, that was Whitsuntide 1924, and in 1925 Herr Doktor died. Would you believe it!

Paula Eckardt, maidservant
Koberwitz Mansion[301]

Countess Johanna von Keyserlingk would gladly have kept Rudolf Steiner for a few more days at Koberwitz after the course ended, for further private discussions and because she saw that his stay there had been beneficial for his health. On 1 June, four days before his departure, she asked him if he would stay on:

I asked Herr Doktor at supper, when his departure was being discussed, whether he could not stay a little longer with us, but he replied that he had to get back to Stuttgart: the young son of Professor Fiechter had driven a gimlet into his eye while playing, and the eye was to be removed immediately; but he hoped it might be saved, and had advised complete bed rest. Yet he added very seriously that he could have no peace until he had seen the child.[302]

The child, Nik Fiechter, and his parents, were waiting in Stuttgart for Rudolf Steiner[303]—as were, likewise, the curative teachers and children at the 'Lauenstein', the first anthroposophical home for children in need of special care, close to Jena. He was due to arrive on the evening of 17 June. Werner Pache who belonged to this small community and cared for the Lauenstein garden among other things, took part in the agricultural lectures and addresses to young people at Koberwitz and Breslau. It was inconceivable for Rudolf Steiner to stay longer in Silesia—quite apart from all the obligations and tasks awaiting him in Dornach.

Shortly before midnight on the last evening at Koberwitz Mansion, after the late return from Breslau, Rudolf Steiner not only told 'cheerful anecdotes' (Koschützki) but also spoke of himself, in a kind of review of the past ten days—and of his own life. According to Guenther Wachsmuth, Rudolf Steiner said in this context:

> In the last two nights, as I now do every week, I had two articles to write here at Koberwitz. I write such articles at various locations, mostly in Dornach. One was for the *Goetheanum* magazine, the other for the newsletter. In *Das Goetheanum* I described a few phases in my biography from the year 1889; and in the newsletter I described the experiences we had here during Whitsun. Thirty-five years lie between these two occurrences—a substantial period which for me, though, represented a kind of rise of our anthroposophical movement. In the earlier time it was not Whitsun but Christmas. I was travelling from Vienna to Hermannstadt in Siebenbürgen, to give some lectures there. So you see, giving lectures was already something that belonged to my spiritual vocation in those days...
>
> They were fine days then too, fine Christmas days. But I have to acknowledge how these two reports—the one from 35 years ago and the one about what has just taken place

now—appear to me, and acknowledge what has happened in the intervening period. Thirty-five years ago very fine things were happening, certainly, within a small group. But now I must continually reflect on what, at that time, did not have a very wide reach—it was hard to approach the world with what one could say at that time—and continually think about how difficult it was back then to bring even a little of such spiritual content to the world... And when the second night arrived, last night, directly preceding today, I had so much to write about that my head was in a whirl and I did not know how I should get it all down in a couple of columns: so many lectures, so many events, and so much that was pushing its way through into these days.

Let us just very briefly review what all this was. Here we have the two poles of spiritual activity: an inner, intimate work which leads one directly into the forming of the spiritual, and how this spiritual reality is itself present here on the earth. And then the other pole, which, I would say, has placed itself alongside the first during these Whitsun days, to the profound satisfaction of anthroposophists now, and which embodies what could be drawn from the world of spirit as an element of practical work to benefit agriculture. In a way you can say that each and every day this path could be traced from the spiritually practical in the morning to the purely spiritual—which is, however, also the fount of all practical work—in the afternoon and evening.[304]

The *'spiritually practical'*—the spiritual founding of a new agriculture—and the *'purely spiritual'*—the karma lectures and Class lessons, and also the talks to young people—had informed Rudolf Steiner's work in Koberwitz, in line with the deeper intentions of the anthroposophical movement and its cultural tasks in the twentieth century.

*

Rudolf Steiner arranged the last meeting with the younger participants of the Agriculture Course for the early morning of the next day—17 June at 7 a.m. Steiner had to wait a long time for the whole group to gather in the lecture room where, over the past few days, a new agriculture had been founded. The delay was extremely embarrassing to those attending, but Rudolf Steiner waited calmly and charitably. He had invited a few additional people to this last meeting, including Elisabeth Vreede. '*What followed was far more than an address: it was a farewell blessing.*'[305]

In his comments, which at times, at least, bore the character of an esoteric lesson, Rudolf Steiner started from young people's search for the spirit in nature, and spoke of the rejection of this search by a civilization whose character was still determined by the past. Nevertheless, said Steiner, this search must succeed, and find the right path to natural processes, to which the element of death also belonged. This death element, he said, was in a certain respect the fundamental condition of natural growth—was connected with a creative spirituality, and indeed with 'divine workings':

Nature builds for itself a wisdom-sustained crystal. The wisdom-sustained crystal can delight us when we wander out into nature. But at the same time we must be clear that gods must die, not an earthly death, but the death of metamorphosis—in other words a transition into unconsciousness—in order to come to life again in the radiant crystal forms. And today we must develop a sense and feeling that when we look upon the sphere of death we find there, shining towards us, the life of gods that has rested unconscious in nature for millennia. In our souls we must find the capacity to feel and discover this light—which can meet us directly from the sun—everywhere also in nature as divine light. Today let us seek to feel and sense, in the whole of heavenly radiant nature surrounding us, the divine soul world that rests through millennia![306]

In modern times, he said, the youth's soul was seeking, unconsciously or subconsciously, for a 'memory' or in other words for a reconnection with the 'divine fount', with the divine-spiritual origin of all earth and star existence:

And this is what one feels when young people seek again for nature today. There lies something of a profoundly earnest world karma in the search for nature and spirit alive in young people today, something of world karma, which is only truly grasped in the soul's deep gravity.[307]

It was of key importance, said Steiner, that the profundity of this search for and 'call' to nature should be properly understood, and increasingly also lived. He pointed out that the 'literary abstract mode' of subjective Romanticism and its affinity with nature at the end of the eighteenth century had brought no remedy. On the contrary, the response to this had assumed forms of demonic materialism in the subsequent period:

Then came the nineteenth century and the fulfilment of that call to nature in the form of knowledge or so-called knowledge of nature, of a repeatedly resounding call to nature in the most rigid, materialistic sense—not just in relation to knowledge either, but in relation to the whole of life. A ghastly fulfilment of Rousseauism emerged in the nineteenth century as a realm of demons, who first giggled when those surrounding Rousseau and the rest of them invoked nature, and then laughed in mockery as they unleashed nature on humanity in ahrimanic form, in the most extreme ahrimanic form. That is the background. And if we seek the intermediate ground, we find the mood of tragic karma, that mood where something lying deeply bedded in the souls of today's youth only emerges into full awareness with the greatest inner soul difficulties: and this is something that has lain there below since the end of Kali Yuga. And then this call or appeal to nature must be found: the ancient workings of the gods must be found in all that earths, streams, airs and fires in nature, and all that shines and has living being above nature. It must be discovered, this ancient spirit of nature.[308]

The Agriculture Course had also in a certain sense been invoking this 'real workings of the gods' in 'all that earths, streams, airs and fires in nature, and all that shines and has living being above nature', as had both the esoteric and exoteric teaching to the 'young doctors' in January and April—in each case in a form adapted to a particular profession. Rudolf Steiner's great 1923 lectures on the seasons of the year and knowledge of nature, which had preceded these latter courses, were also part of this context. The esoteric lessons of the 'First Class' were also a path of schooling for perceiving and living with the elements and the hierarchies. Although Rudolf Steiner did not speak of this, he fervently hoped that the younger generation would find and pursue this path—and would thus find deeper understanding of themselves and their own longings, instead of falling prey, once again, to seductive and alienating powers:

[...] How can one avoid the rain, as it were, of wild demons, but also the torrent of wild illusions that followed the invocation of nature in the nineteenth century? This should not happen in such a way! The twentieth century must not become an age of materialism! And thus the voice of karma calls within young people's souls today: If you allow the twentieth century to be materialistic as the nineteenth century was, then you will have lost much not only of your own humanity but also that of all civilization.[309]

In June 1924, eight months before his own death, Rudolf Steiner was clearly fully aware of the forthcoming crises of the twentieth century. He knew that the small group of young farmers and gardeners sitting in front of him would neither determine nor alter the fate of Central Europe and all civilization. Nevertheless a great deal depended, evidently, on the spirituality of the future being taken up and realized by small communities—both in general terms and in core areas of life such as farming.

While young people interested in anthroposophy at that time were, in Steiner's view, still vague in their feelings about many things, nevertheless he could see that they had a certain inner certainty, one 'which is not yet wholly light-filled, but bears a certain strength within it'. This 'strength' needed developing and even schooling, through working to perceive and understand nature:

> But this strength should and must not be broken. Anthroposophy wishes, for its part, to do something here too, because it believes it can hear the tangible spirit in all small details: in plant roots, in the deeds of the light above the plants, in the soulful blessings of warmth passing through the plants; because it believes that all of this has also, at the same time, been vouchsafed to humanity as an exhortation. And likewise the realm of animals, because it believes that much needs to be healed in this animal nature. Animals exist on earth for the human being's sake. In order for us to conduct ourselves rightly towards the animals and

all nature, it is necessary for us to feel, sense and ultimately also perceive and know each individual spiritual being everywhere in nature.[310]

According to Rudolf Steiner, it was not a matter of speaking in general terms about the spirit, but rather:

> to seek spiritual workings right into specific measures taken in agriculture and other modes of engagement with nature today. This is why my deepest soul felt a sympathetic affinity when your message reached me that we might exchange ideas on this or that theme.[311]

*

Following these words, the participants sitting in a semicircle around Rudolf Steiner engaged in conversation. Their views were not taken down in shorthand—but Rudolf Steiner was moved by them:

> Our younger friends [...] spoke from the depths of their hearts about their longing to approach, through their work and creativity, insights from the sphere of spirit which connect the human being with the active forces of nature. This was a conversation from the inmost soul of youth which desires to get beyond unfruitful materialism. Such materialism does not connect us with nature but separates us from it and condemns our work to fruitlessness.[312]

Reviewing how this session continued, Rudolf Steiner wrote: 'At this gathering of young people I was able to point to paths whereby this longing could move towards a goal.'[313] In the second part of his address (after the comments and reports) Rudolf Steiner said that he had tried in the Agriculture Course to take full account of the longing 'to approach, through their work and creativity, insights from the sphere of spirit which connect the human being with the active forces of nature'. The 'spirit that is only thought', he said, remains alien to nature—and must become an inwardly felt and 'grasped spirit':

> That is why I tried in this course, to find words as it were out of actual experience. There is no other way of finding the spirit today than by seeking a means to clothe it, in turn, in naturally given words. Thereby feelings will also grow strong again. You see, if you think about it, you transform what one can already know today—for the Michael era has arrived—what apparently only lives in ideas, into real reverence, and then you are on the best path of all. You are on the best possible path if you transform things into reverence. Yes indeed, all kinds of things can then emerge! After all, meditating means transforming what one knows into reverence, especially in quite specific, tangible things.[314]

Finally, on the morning of 17 June, Rudolf Steiner spoke again about the development of anthroposophy at the end of the nineteenth and beginning of the twentieth centuries. He spoke of its often obstructed reception, its rejection by civil society and the failed attempt to intellectualize it or make it seem alien—but also of his hope for the current young generation. Rudolf Steiner ended with broad panoramas, once again emphasizing a devotion to Michael and the approaching future:

> For young people today it is not a matter of transforming anthroposophy into ever greater abstraction, into ideas, concepts and even whole fields of academic study. Now a younger generation has arrived which wishes only to feel and experience all this: in deeds—in insight into nature. But

one cannot stay put there—and this is something I'd like to emphasize particularly today.

It was said that the Michael sword is being fashioned and forged. But something else is involved also—the fact now simply exists in the occult dimension of the world that what must be created as Michael sword must really be carried to, and forged upon, an altar that really could not be outwardly visible, that must lie beneath the earth, really beneath the earth. There it must be found by receptive souls. What is needed is for you to participate by helping increasing numbers of souls to find the sword of Michael. And it is not enough simply to forge it, but what really first counts is that it should be found. As young people, be strong and at the same time humble in your self-confidence that you are in fact karmically called to bear the Michael sword into the world, to seek it and find it. Then you will have what you seek in such gatherings as the one today. Then you will also recognize what I had to tell you about anthroposophy, about the difficulties of those caught between their doctoral exam and retirement plan. And you will see from this, but now in an entirely instinctive way, so that the spirit of abstraction, this terrible ahrimanic spirit, cannot touch you too—think of it in mighty images—that in the strivings of young people two words have combined which were no longer understood in the nineteenth century.

If one hears the word 'Wandervogel' [literally 'wanderbirds'] you gain a sense from it, a question as to whether today anyone, even a well-travelled person, really any longer knows what wandering meant in ancient times. We have to get back to pictorial soul experience. When someone ponders the world of birds today, does he still know that one must first undergo what Siegfried underwent in order to understand the language of the birds? Wander-birds—Odin, Siegfried: this is what one needs to feel and understand once again. One must first find the path from the abstract sense of the 'Wandervogel' to the figure of Odin who weaves in the earth organism's wind, clouds and waves; and to the hidden language of the birds with which one must become acquainted by enlivening within oneself a Siegfried memory and the Siegfried sword, which was merely the prophetic prefiguring of the Michael sword. One must find one's way from the wanderer to Odin just as, opening oneself and growing light of heart again, one can believe again in the birds' hidden language. All of you feel the path from the 'Wandervogel' to Odin, to Siegfried. And if one can sense this deep in one's soul, then one will also find the means to feel nature, and will gain knowledge of these things. And if, besides this, one manages also to dream a little, one will be able to live in nature with the dreams of heaven.

This is what we should initially not reflect on but instead feel and sense thoroughly. If you do so, you will form a community that speaks to your heart, in which, passing through various stages, you will find precisely what you seek. Let us give life to this in our awareness, let us fill our souls with it![315]

*

Wilhelm Rath, a participant whom Steiner had jokingly referred to as a 'Landstreicher' [vagrant] and who later became a farmer, wrote:

This conversation of Rudolf Steiner with the young people, to which he gave the character of an esoteric Class lesson, because he recognized the holy seriousness of our hearts, became for us the knowledge that *there is also a path to the spirit through work, through practical work.*[316]

After his unforgettably 'admonishing and at the same time love-emanating talk'[317] Rudolf Steiner walked round the circle and took his leave from each person: 'He went to each one and not only gave them his hand, but took every hand that was offered him in both of his [...]'[318]

After this, Rudolf Steiner had another long talk with Johanna von Keyserlingk, gave Carl von Keyserlingk the letter for Eliza von Moltke, visited the mansion's kitchen to thank the staff, and wrote in the guest book:

With love for the house of Koberwitz,
The seat of good anthroposophists,
We came to search anew
For the hearts both faithful and true,
The active spirit to rouse
Which lives within this house
By the love which here we found
We are to each other bound.

With most heartfelt thanks
Rudolf Steiner

After that he handed the visitor's book to Frau Marie Steiner and said: 'So—now you add a meaningful thought.' 'No,' she answered, I won't do that, I shall only add my name, I prefer to remain in your shadow.'

All the inhabitants of the house stood in the hall and at the door during the leave-taking. Rudolf Steiner went up to each one individually, including the manservant and the maidservant, and held out his hand to them without saying anything. His thrice-spoken, friendly 'Auf Wiedersehen' resounded no more.[319] We were touched by the breath of departure.

The Whitsuntide gathering at Koberwitz had come to an end.[320]

Marie Steiner also gave her room-maidservant the book *Knowledge of the Higher Worlds* containing a dedication from Rudolf Steiner; then she was driven to Dresden by Andreas von Grunelius. Rudolf Steiner himself travelled by car to Breslau with Guenther Wachsmuth, Elisabeth Vreede and the Keyserlingks, from where his train took him to Jena, to the 'Lauenstein' and the children in need of special care.

The Agriculture Course was a 'mighty affair' as a servant of the Keyserlingks, Paula Eckardt, later said when looking back on it.[321] Rudolf Steiner agreed with her:

[...] I still remember vividly [...] how, during the journey between Breslau and Jena, after pondering in quiet reflection on the conference, he suddenly said with strong, joyful tone: '*Now we have accomplished that important work as well.*' Seldom have I seen Rudolf Steiner so joyfully moved and visibly delighted as at this moment after the Agriculture Course. (Guenther Wachsmuth[322])

Notes and References

(For technical reasons, two separate English editions of Rudolf Steiner's agricultural lectures have been quoted in the text. They are referred to below as *Agriculture* and *Agriculture Course*. Full publication details can be found on page 193.)

1. Rudolf Meyer, in: Keyserlingk, Adalbert, p. 10
2. Koepf, Herbert H. and von Plato, Bodo, p. 51
3. *Agriculture* (GA 327), p. 3
4. *Agriculture Course* (GA 327), p. 111
5. *Agriculture*, p. 10
6. *Agriculture Course*, p. 132 f.
7. Ibid, p. 76
8. Ibid, p. 28
9. GA 217a, p. 157
10. Ehrenfried Pfeiffer: 'Rudolf Steiners landwirtschaftlicher Impuls' in: Krück von Poturzyn, p. 173
11. Ibid, p. 179
12. GA 239, p. 267 f.
13. Paula Eckardt, in: Keyserlingk, Adalbert, p. 97
14. Ibid, p. 10
15. GA 310, p. 75
16. *Agriculture*, p. 6
17. *Agriculture Course*, p. 18
18. Quoted in Vollmer, p. 85
19. Ibid, p. 38
20. GA 260a, p. 319
21. Ita Wegman Archive, Arlesheim
22. Letter from Ludwig Engel to Ita Wegman on 17 June 1924. Ita Wegman Archive
23. In: Keyserlingk, Adalbert, p. 83
24. *Agriculture*, p. 2

25. Almar von Wistinghausen: *Erinnerungen an den Anfang der biologisch-dynamischen Wirtschaftsweise. Vom landwirtschaftlichen Auftrag Rudolf Steiners und von seinen Schülern.* Darmstadt 1982, p. 23

26. Manfred Klett: 'Der landwirtschftlicher Kurs—ein Pfingstereignis'. In: Stefan O. Mahlich (ed.): *Identität und Offenheit auf der Suche nach einer neuen Landwirtschaftskultur.* Dornach 2006, p. 64

27. Ibid

28. *Agriculture*, p. 5. Author's emphasis

29. Ibid, p. 9

30. *Agriculture Course*, p. 61

31. Koepf, Herbert H. and von Plato, Bodo

32. Ibid, p. 50

33. *Agriculture*, p. 2

34. *Agriculture Course*, p. 6

35. Cf. Peter Selg: *Rudolf Steiner—zur Gestalt eines geistigen Lehrers. Eine Einführung.* Dornach 2007, p. 60 f. (Forthcoming English edition: *Rudolf Steiner as a Spiritual Teacher*, SteinerBooks, Great Barrington 2010.)

36. Rudolf Steiner: *Briefe I 1881–1891. Mit einer 'Skizze eines Lebensabrisses'.* Dornach 1955, p. 34

37. GA 262, p. 16 (transcript for Eduard Schuré, September 1907)

38. Cf. Peter Selg: *'Wie eine Art Gottesdienst'. Rudolf Steiner, die Oberuferer Spiele und das Weihnachtsfest.* Stuttgart 2008

39. GA 38, p. 24

40. *Agriculture Course*, p. 84

41. GA 107, p. 159

42. GA 327, p. 166 f.

43. GA 77a, p. 49

44. GA 266/3, p. 428

45. GA 254, p. 196

46. Cf. Johanna von Keyserlingk: 'My First Encounters with Rudolf Steiner' in: Keyserlingk, Adalbert, p. 20 f.

47. Ibid, p. 29

48. Keyserlingk, Johanna, p. 71

49. In: Keyserlingk, Adalbert, p. 43

50. Letter from Carl von Keyserlingk to Rudolf Steiner on 13 August 1920. Rudolf Steiner Archive, Dornach

51. Keyserlingk, Johanna, p. 25

52. Letter from Carl von Keyserlingk to Rudolf Steiner on 13 August 1920. Rudolf Steiner Archive, Dornach

53. Ibid

54. In: Keyserlingk, Adalbert, pp. 101–102

55. GA 260a, p. 22

56. In: Keyserlingk, Adalbert, p. 59

57. GA 217a, p. 169

58. Ibid

59. GA 327, p. 229

60. Rudolf Meyer: 'Pfingsttagung in Koberwitz 1924'. In: Beltle/ Vierl, p. 441

61. Rudolf Steiner Archive

62. Ibid

63. Ibid

64. Ehrenfried Pfeiffer: 'Aus meinem Leben' (1958). In: Thomas Meyer (ed.): *Ein Leben für den Geist. Ehrenfried Pfeiffer (1899–1961)*. Basel 1999, p. 119 f.

65. Ehrenfried Pfeiffer, quoted in: Alla Selawry: *Ehrenfried Pfeiffer. Pionier spiritueller Forschung und Praxis. Begegnungen und Briefwechsel*. Dornach 1987, p. 62 [English edition: *Ehrenfried Pfeiffer*, Mercury Press, 1992]

66. Ibid (Steiner), p. 26

67. Ehrenfried Pfeiffer: 'Rudolf Steiners landwirtschaftlicher Impuls'. In: Krück von Poturzyn, p. 173 f.

68. Wachsmuth, p. 505

69. Ibid, p. 505

70. Ehrenfried Pfeiffer: 'Rudolf Steiners landwirtschaftlicher Impuls'. In: Krück von Poturzyn, p. 171.

71. Ibid

72. Cf. Peter Selg (ed.): *Eugen Kolisko, Das Wesen und die*

Behandlung der Maul- und Klauenseuche. Pionierversuche 1920–25. Dornach 2001.

73. Ehrenfried Pfeiffer: 'Rudolf Steiners landwirtschaftlicher Impuls'. In: Krück von Poturzyn, p. 172

74. Johann Simon Streicher: 'Die Angaben Dr. Rudolf Steiners betreffs Verwendung von mineralischen Düngern in der Landwirtschaft, insbesondere über die Notwendigkeit einer Magnesia Düngung' (1941). Typescript. Rudolf Steiner Archive, Dornach

75. Bartsch, p. 4

76. Ibid. In this obituary for his brother, Hellmuth Bartsch quotes from a letter from Immanuel Voegele dated 2 March 1951: '. . . and I couldn't think of anyone apart from Rudolf Steiner who would have been able to help. We needed a course similar to that given for doctors, teachers etc. I still recall clearly how you responded to my reflective, questioning stance in a spontaneous and impulsive way, and said, more or less: Let's go for it and get on with it!'

77. Rudolf Steiner Archive, Dornach

78. Ibid

79. Quoted in Bartsch, p. 4

80. Ibid

81. Johanna von Keyserlingk, in: Keyserlingk, Adalbert, p.60

82. Ibid, p. 105

83. Quoted in Karl Lang: *Lebensbegegnungen.* Benenfeld 1972, p. 6

84. Quoted in GA 259, p. 863

85. Rudolf Steiner Archive

86. Ehrenfried Pfeiffer: 'Rudolf Steiners landwirtschaftlicher Impuls'. In: Krück von Poturzyn, p. 172

87. *Agriculture*, p. 2

88. In: Keyserlingk, Adalbert, p. 105

89. Rudolf Steiner Archive, Dornach

90. Ibid

91. Ibid

92. Ibid

93. Ibid

94. Ibid

95. Letter from Carl von Keyserlingk to Guenther Wachsmuth on 12 May 1924, Rudolf Steiner Archive, Dornach

96. Archive at the Goetheanum

97. Rudolf Steiner Archive

98. GA 233a, p. 134 f.

99. Rudolf Steiner: *Die verborgenen Seiten des Menschendaseins und der Christus-Impuls.* Dornach 1939, p. 33

100. Cf. also, among others, Peter Selg: *Anfänge anthroposophischer Heilkunst,* Dornach 2000; and Peter Selg: *'Ich bin für Fortschreiten.' Ita Wegman und die Medizinische Sektion.* Dornach 2002 (Chapter 1)

101. GA 262, p. 328

102. Annemarie Dubach-Donath: *Die Kunst der Eurythmie. Erinnerungen.* Dornach 1983, p. 124

103. GA 257, p. 11

104. GA 259, p. 208

105. Ibid, p. 484

106. Ibid, p. 344

107. GA 260a, p. 371

108. Ibid, p. 434

109. GA 260, p. 212

110. Ibid, p. 93 f.

111. Cf. Peter Selg: *The Figure of Christ. Rudolf Steiner and the spiritual intention behind the Goetheanum's central work of art.* Temple Lodge 2009

112. GA 233a, p. 134 f.

113. Christoph Lindenberg: *Rudolf Steiner. Eine Chronik. 1861– 1925.* Stuttgart 1988, p. 504

114. Cf. Peter Selg: *'Ich bleibe bei Ihnen'. Rudolf Steiner und Ita Wegman.* München 1907—Dornach 1923–1925. Stuttgart 2007; and Peter Selg: *Rudolf Steiner und die Freie Hochschule für Geisteswissenschaft. Die Begründung der 'Ersten Klasse'.* Arlesheim 2008

115. Wachsmuth, p. 547 f.
116. GA 186, p. 122
117. Keyserlingk, Alexander, in: Keyserlingk, Adalbert, p. 93
118. GA 327, p. 236
119. Ita Wegman: notebook entry (1931). Ita Wegman Archive
120. Cf. Peter Selg: *'Die Medizin muss Ernst machen mit dem geistigen Leben'. Rudolf Steiners Hochschulkurse für die 'jungen Mediziner'.* Dornach 2006
121. GA 260a, p. 489
122. GA 223, p. 86
123. GA 224, p. 14
124. GA 239, p. 80
125. Cf. Peter Selg (ed.): Ita Wegman: *Erinnerungen an Rudolf Steiner.* Arlesheim 2009
126. GA 236, p. 244
127. Ibid, p. 241
128. Ibid, p. 248
129. Ibid, p. 252
130. Johanna von Keyserlingk, in: Adalbert von Keyserlingk, p. 60–61
131. Ibid, p. 61
132. Keyserlingk, Johanna, p. 3
133. Kurt von Wistinghausen: 'Die Breslauer Jugendansprachen Rudolf Steiners, Juni 1924', in: GA 217a, p. 212
134. In: von Keyserling, Adalbert, p. 61
135. Keyserlingk, Johanna, p. 3
136. Cf. Peter Selg: *The Figure of Christ. Rudolf Steiner and the spiritual intention behind the Goetheanum's central work of art.* Temple Lodge 2009
137. Johanna von Keyserlingk, in: Keyserlingk, Adalbert
138. Ibid, p. 106
139. *Agriculture Course*, p. 62
140. Kurt von Wistinghausen: 'Die Breslauer Jugendansprachen Rudolf Steiners, Juni 1924', in: GA 217a, p. 212
141. Keyserlingk, Johanna, p. 4

142. Keyserlingk, Alexander, in: Keyserlingk, Adalbert, p. 106
143. Rath, Wilhelm, in: ibid, p. 130
144. Rudolf von Koschützki: 'Erinnerungen eines Priesters'. In: Beltle/Vierl, p. 316
145. Keyserlingk, Johanna, p. 5
146. *Agriculture Course*, p. 17
147. Ibid, p. 17
148. Ibid,
149. Ibid, p. 21
150. Letter of 10 June 1924, Ita Wegman Archive, Arlesheim
151. GA 327, p. 236
152. Keyserlingk, Johanna, p. 7
153. Ibid, p. 7 f.
154. Karin Ruths-Hoffman in: Keyserlingk, Adalbert
155. Rudolf von Koschützki: 'Erinnerungen eines Priesters'. In: Beltle/Vierl, p. 316
156. Ita Wegman Archive, Arlesheim
157. Keyserlingk, Adalbert, p. 69
158. Keyserlingk, Johanna, p. 16
159. Ita Wegman Archive, Arlesheim
160. Ibid
161. Rudolf Meyer, in: Adalbert, Keyserlingk, p. 3 f.
162. In: Keyserlingk, Johanna, p. 78
163. Ibid, p. 9
164. Ita Wegman Archive, Arlesheim
165. Keyserlingk, Johanna, p. 10
166. *Agriculture*, p. 2
167. GA 229, p. 19
168. Keyserlingk, Johanna, p. 10 f.
169. In: Keyserlingk, Adalbert, p. 66 f.
170. Rudolf Steiner, GA 316, p. 70 f.
171. In: Keyserlingk, Adalbert, p. 69
172. Keyserlingk, Johanna, p. 42
173. In: Keyserlingk, Adalbert, p. 5
174. In: Keyserlingk, Johanna, p. 75

175. In: Keyserlingk, Adalbert, p. 121 f.
176. Letter from Ludwig Engel to Ita Wegman on 27 May 1924. Ita Wegman Archive, Arlesheim
177. In: Keyserlingk, Adalbert, p. 122
178. Cf. Ludwig Engel: Patientenvorstellungen in Koberwitz. In: *Rundbrief der Medizinischen Sektion*, no. 19/1996
179. Ita Wegman Archive, Arlesheim
180. Ludwig Engel in: Keyserlingk, Adalbert, p. 123
181. Ibid, p. 63
182. Ibid, p. 73
183. Cf. J.E. Zeylmans van Emmichoven: *Who Was Ita Wegman*, vol. 1, Mercury Press, USA 1995
184. Keyserlingk, Alexander, in Keyserlingk, Adalbert, p. 106
185. Paula Eckhardt, in: ibid, p. 110
186. Luise von Zastrow, in: ibid, p. 114
187. Keyserlingk, Johanna, in: ibid, p. 70
188. Keyserlingk, Johanna, in: ibid, p. 78
189. Keyserlingk, Johanna, p. 33
190. Ibid, p. 34. Cf. Thomas Meyer (ed.): *Helmuth von Moltke 1948–1916. Dokumente zu seinem Leben und Wirken.* Vol. 2: *Briefe von Rudolf Steiner an Helmuth und Eliza von Moltke.* Basel 1993, p. 298 f.
191. In Keyserlingk, Johanna, p. 31
192. Moritz Bartsch: 'Ein Schlesier berichtet'. In: Beltle/Vierl, p. 474
193. Keyserlingk, Johanna, in: Keyserlingk, Adalbert, p. 75 f.
194. Engel, Ludwig in: ibid, p. 127
195. *Agriculture*, p. 6
196. Rudolf von Koschützki: 'Erinnerungen eines Priesters.' In: Beltle/Vierl, p. 317
197. Wachsmuth, p. 586
198. Ita Wegman Archive, Arlesheim
199. GA 327, p. 85
200. Ibid, p. 86
201. *Agriculture Course*, p. 65

202. GA 327, p.179
203. *Agriculture Course*, p. 114
204. *Agriculture Course*, p. 27
205. Ibid, p. 20 f.
206. Ibid, p. 89
207. Ibid, p. 144, author's emphasis
208. Ibid, p. 36
209. Ibid, p. 40
210. Ibid, p. 54
211. Ibid, p. 127 f.
212. Ibid, p. 55
213. Ibid, p. 69
214. Ibid, p. 71
215. *Agriculture*, p. 2
216. Ibid, p. 3, author's emphasis
217. *Agriculture Course*, p. 50
218. Ibid, p. 118
219. Ibid, p. 90
220. Ibid, p. 118
221. Ibid, p. 25
222. Ibid, p. 120
223. Ibid
224. Ibid
225. GA 17, p. 39
226. GA 103, p. 201
227. Rudolf von Koschützki: 'Erinnerungen eines Priesters.' In: Beltle/Vierl, p. 316
228. Ibid
229. *Agriculture Course*, p. 77
230. Ibid, p. 51
231. Ibid, p. 48 f.
232. Ibid, p. 51 f.
233. Ibid, p. 84
234. GA 26, p. 118
235. *Agriculture Course*, p. 82 f.

236. Ibid, p. 85
237. Ibid, p. 34
238. Ibid, p. 94 f.
239. Ibid, p. 149
240. Ibid, p. 39 f.
241. Ibid, 111 f.
242. GA 316, p. 137
243. Cf. Peter Selg: *Die Briefkorrespondenz der 'jungen Mediziner'. Eine dokumentarische Studie zur Rezeption von Rudolf Steiners 'Jungmedizinerkursen'*. Dornach 2005
244. *Agriculture Course*, p. 62 f.
245. *Agriculture*, p. 4
246. *Agriculture Course*, p. 60
247. Ibid, p. 149 f.
248. Wilhelm Rath: 'Anthroposophischer Landbau'. In: Beltle/ Vierl, p. 464
249. Ibid, p. 443
250. Ita Wegman Archive, Arlesheim
251. Moritz Bartsch: 'Ein Schlesier berichtet' in: Beltle/Vierl, p. 477
252. GA 239, p. 123
253. Ibid, p. 129, author's emphasis
254. Ibid, p. 143
255. Ibid, p. 144
256. Ibid, p. 145
257. Ibid, p. 149 f.
258. Ibid, p. 150
259. Ibid, p. 152
260. Ibid, p. 137
261. Ibid, p. 139, author's emphasis
262. Ibid, p. 182 f.
263. Ibid, 244 f.
264. Keyserlingk, Adalbert, p. 4
265. Ibid, p 74
266. GA 260a, p. 318
267. Ibid

268. Ibid, p. 105
269. GA 217a, p. 214
270. Ibid, p. 127
271. Ibid, p. 130
272. Kurt von Wistinghausen, in: Keyserlingk, Johanna, p. 74
273. GA 217a, p. 137
274. Ibid, p. 139
275. Ibid, p. 142
276. Ibid, p. 141
277. Ibid, p. 147
278. Cf. GA 258
279. GA 217a, p. 142
280. GA 260a, p. 74 f.
281. GA 316, p. 79
282. GA 217a, p. 144 f. (author's emphasis)
283. Ibid, p. 145 (author's emphasis)
284. Ibid, p. 145 f.
285. Ibid, p. 148
286. Quoted in Vollmer, p. 63
287. GA 217a, p. 154
288. Ibid, p. 155
289. Quoted by Peter Selg: 'Goethe's Naturwissenschaft als objektiver Realismus' in: Peter Selg: *Vom Logos menschlicher Physis. Die Entfaltung einer anthroposophischen Human-physiologie im Werk Rudolf Steiners.* Dornach 2000, p. 51 f.
290. GA 12, p. 37
291. GA 43, p. 97
292. GA 217a, p. 151
293. Ibid, p. 151 f.
294. In: Keyserlingk, Johanna, p. 74
295. GA 217a, p. 214
296. Ibid, p. 159
297. Ibid
298. In: Keyserlingk, Adalbert, p. 5
299. GA 217a, p. 160

300. In: Keyserlingk, Johanna, p. 74

301. In: Keyserlingk, Adalbert, p. 136

302. Keyserlingk, Johanna, p. 32

303. Cf. Nik Fiechter: A healing meditation for a child, in: *Mitteilungen aus der anthroposophischen Arbeit in Deutschland.* No. 131/1980

304. Wachsmuth, p. 587 f.

305. Kurt von Wistinghausen: Die Breslauer Jugendansprachen Rudolf Steiners, Juni 1924. In: Beltle/Vierl, p. 457

306. GA 217a, p. 162 f.

307. Ibid, p. 163

308. Ibid, p. 164 f.

309. Ibid, p. 165

310. Ibid, p. 164

311. Ibid, p. 166

312. Ibid, p. 161

313. Ibid

314. Ibid, p. 169 f.

315. Ibid, p. 174 ff.

316. In: Keyserlingk, Adalbert, p. 132

317. Kurt von Wistinghausen: Die Breslauer Jugendansprachen Rudolf Steiners, Juni 1924. In: Beltle/Vierl, p. 458

318. Johanna von Keyserlingk, in: Keyserlingk, Adalbert, p. 82

319. The implication is that he did not use the word 'Auf Wiedersehen' because he would not see them again

320. Luise von Zastrow, in: Keyserlingk, Adalbert, p. 115 f.

321. Paula Eckardt in: Keyserlingk, Adalbert, p. 112

322. Wachsmuth, p. 593

Bibliography

Frequently cited works:

Bartsch, Hellmut: 'Dr Erhard Bartsch. Gedenken an den Mitbegründer der biologisch-dynamischen Landwirtschaft. Ein Lebens– und Wirkensbild.' In: *Lebendige Erde*, series 12, 1961

Beltle, Erika and Vierl, Kurt (ed.): *Erinnerungen an Rudolf Steiner.* Stuttgart 1979.

Keyserlingk, Adalbert von (ed.): *The Birth of a New Agriculture. Koberwitz 1924.* Temple Lodge 1999

Keyserlingk, Johanna von: *Zwölf Tage um Rudolf Steiner. (Edited version included in above.)*

Koepf, Herbert H. and von Plato, Bodo: *Die biologisch-dynamische Wirtschaftsweise im 20. Jahrhundert.* Dornach 2001

Krück von Poturzyn, M. J. (ed.): *Wir erlebten Rudolf Steiner. Erinnerungen seiner Schüler.* Stuttgart 1967 (English edition: *A Man Before Others.* Rudolf Steiner Press, 1993)

Vollmer, Hanna: *Chronik 1924.* Gütersloh/Munich 2004

Wachsmuth, Guenther: *Rudolf Steiners Erdenleben und Wirken. Von der Jahrhundertwende bis zum Tode. Die Geburt der Geisteswissenschaft. Eine Biographie.* Dornach 1951 (English edition: *The Life and Work of Rudolf Steiner.* Whittier Books, New York 1955)

Works by Rudolf Steiner

Volumes in the Collected Works (GA) mentioned and cited in the text, all published by Rudolf Steiner Verlag, Dornach, except for (the two English versions of) GA 327:

AP/SB = Anthroposophic Press/SteinerBooks, USA
RSP   = Rudolf Steiner Press, UK

GA

12   *Stufen der höheren Erkenntnis* (1993). *Stages of Higher Knowledge* (AP)

26   *Anthroposophische Leitsätze* (1998). *Anthroposophical Leading Thoughts* (RSP)

38   *Briefe,* vol. 1: 1881–1890 (1985)

77a *Die Aufgabe der Anthroposophie gegenüber Wissenschaft und Technik* (1977)

103 *Das Johannes-Evangelium* (1995). *The Gospel of St. John* (AP)

107 *Geisteswissenschaftliche Menschenkunde*

186 *Die soziale Grundforderung unserer Zeit—in geänderter Zeitlage* (1990)

217a *Die Erkenntnis-Aufgabe der Jugend* (1981). *Youth and the Etheric Heart* (SB)

223 *Der Jahreskreislauf als Atmungsvorgang der Erde und die vier grossen Festeszeiten* (1990). *The Cycle of the Year* (AP)

224 *Die menschliche Seele in ihrem Zusammenhang mit göttlich-geistigen Individualitäten* (1992)

229 *Das Miterleben des Jahreslaufes in vier kosmischen Imaginationen* (1999). *The Four Seasons and the Archangels* (RSP)

233a *Mysterienstätten des Mittelalters* (1991). *Rosicrucianism and Modern Initiation* (RSP). *The Easter Festival in the Evolution of the Mysteries* (RSP/AP)

236 *Esoterische Betrachtungen karmischer Zusammenhänge.* Vol. II (1998). *Karmic Relationships,* Vol. 2 (RSP)

239 *Esoterische Betrachtungen karmischer Zusammenhänge.* Vol. V (1995). *Karmic Relationships,* Vol. 5 (RSP)

254 *Die okkulte Bewegung im neunzehnten Jahrhundert und ihre Beziehung zur Weltkultur* (1986). *The Occult Movement in the Nineteenth Century* (RSP)

257 *Anthroposophische Gemeinschaftsbildung* (1989). *Awakening to Community* (AP)

258 *Die Geschichte und die Bedingungen der anthroposophischen Gesellschaft. Vom Goetheanumbrand zur Weihnachtstagung* (1991). *The Anthroposophic Movement* (RSP)

259 *Das Schicksalsjahr 1923 in der Geschichte der Anthroposophischen Gesellschaft. Vom Goetheanumbrand zur Weihnachtstagung* (1991)

260a *Die Konstitution der Allgemeinen Anthroposophischen Gesellschaft und der Freien Hochschule für Geisteswissenschaft* (1987)

260 *Die Weihnachtstagung zur Begründung der Allgemeinen Anthroposophischen Gesellschaft* (1987). *The Christmas Conference 1923/1924* (AP)

262 Rudolf Steiner/Marie Steiner-von Sivers: *Briefwechsel und Dokumente* (2002). *Correspondence and Documents* (RSP/ AP)

266/3 *Aus den Inhalten der esoterischen Stunden*. Vol. III (1998). *Esoteric Lessons*, Vol. 3 (SB)

310 *Der pädagogische Wert der Menschenerkenntnis und der Kulturwert der Pädagogik* (1989). *Human Values in Education* (SB)

316 *Meditative Betrachtungen und Anleitungen zur Vertiefung der Heilkunst* (2003). *Course for Young Doctors* (Mercury Press)

317 *Heilpädagogischer Kurs* (1995). *Education for Special Needs* (RSP)

327 *Geisteswissenschaftliche Grundlagen zum Gedeihen der Landwirtschaft. Landwirtschaftlicher Kurs* (1999)
Agriculture Course, Rudolf Steiner Press (2004)
Agriculture, Biodynamic Farming and Gardening Association Inc., USA (1993)

343 *Vorträge und Kurse über christlich-religiöses Wirken* (1993)

Also available from Temple Lodge by Peter Selg:

The Figure of Christ
Rudolf Steiner and the spiritual intention behind the Goetheanum's central work of art

'Yes, that is the Christ. This is how my spiritual eye perceived him in Palestine.'—Rudolf Steiner, speaking of his sculpted figure of Christ

Rudolf Steiner referred to the wooden 'group' sculpture of the figure of Christ surrounded by adversary spiritual beings as the *centre* of the first Goetheanum. Steiner even told the architect of the second Goetheanum that the sculpture he made with Edith Maryon should occupy the same central position 'as in the first building'.

What was Rudolf Steiner's essential aim for the sculptural group within the Mystery building he conceived, and why did he regard it as the *crown* of the building? What were Steiner's intentions— and, specifically, what were the spiritual aims behind this remarkable depiction of Christ?

Rudolf Steiner described the core task of anthroposophical spiritual science as preparing for Christ's reappearance in the etheric realm. The Christ he sculpted was not the possession of a specific community with a religious world view, but rather a being active throughout humanity, and thus 'a figure of the future'.

In this focused and powerful short book, Peter Selg engages with these highly-contemporary issues, providing thoughtful insights and answers that point to mysteries of the future involving humanity's further development and the transforming of evil.

80pp; £7.95; ISBN 978 1 906999 01 8

Ita Wegman Institute

for Basic Research into Anthroposophy

PFEFFINGER WEG 1 A CH-4144 ARLESHEIM, SWITZERLAND
www.wegmaninstitut.ch

The Ita Wegman Institute for Basic Research into Anthroposophy is a non-profit research and teaching organization. It undertakes basic research into the lifework of Dr. Rudolf Steiner (1861–1925) and the application of Anthroposophy in specific areas of life, especially medicine, education, and curative education. Work carried out by the Institute is supported by a number of foundations and organizations and an international group of friends and supporters. The Director of the Institute is Prof. Dr. Peter Selg.